W9-DDH-044

Island Trek

ISLAND TREK

An historical and geographical tour of Seal Island, Nova Scotia, as seen by the author and related to him by Mrs. Winifred Crowell Hamilton who lived on the Island all of her lifetime. Places and dates are reasonably accurate. Dialogue is fictional on occasion to make for more interesting reading.

by

Walter W. Hichens

LANCELOT PRESS

Hantsport, Nova Scotia

ACKNOWLEDGEMENTS

Island Trek could not have been written without the information provided by Winifred Hamilton and the encouragement to write the book given by many friends and relatives. Thanks are due to Mary Nickerson, daughter of Mrs. Hamilton, fishermen, and Barrington and Clark's Harbour residents, who furnished bits of information incorporated in *Island Trek*, and to Ethel R. Smith, the author's sister, who typed the manuscript for publication.

ISBN 0-88999-169-3

All rights reserved. No part of this book may be reproduced in any form without written permission of the publishers except brief quotations embodied in critical articles or reviews.

Published 1982
  Second printing December 1982
  Third printing May 1985
  Fourth printing July 1988

LANCELOT PRESS LIMITED, Hantsport, N.S.

Office and plant situated on Highway No. 1, 1/2 mile east of Hantsport

DEDICATION

Dedicated to Winnifred Crowell Hamilton who was so helpful in supplying facts and dates for the writing of Island Trek, and in memory of Dr. Ben Hichens, my grandfather, whose life and Christian testimony was an inspiration to all who knew him.

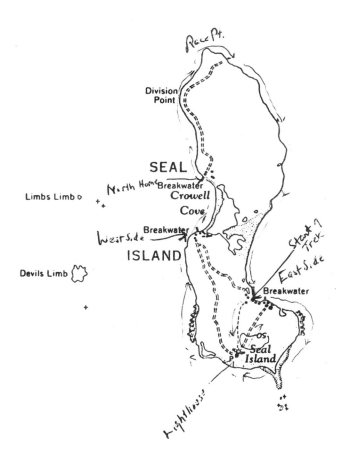

Race Pt.

Division
Point

SEAL

Limbs Limb o

North Home Breakwater

*Crowell
Cove*

Weirside Breakwater

ISLAND

Devils Limb

Start ?
Trek

EastSide

Breakwater

os

*Seal
Island*

Lighthouse

+Elbow Rock

6

ISLAND TREK

It was still dark when she awoke. Perhaps the dog, shifting on the rug beside her bed, the rustle of the hemlock just outside the window or the anticipation of the day ahead brought her out of her sleep, but whatever, she knew that she would not doze off again. No matter how long before daylight it might be, she was awake for the day.

She lay there snug in the middle of the bed, content with the blanket over her even though it was the second day of July, and she hàd known this time of year to be warm and muggy. She hoped the day would be a bit on the cool side. It could be a bit uncomfortable before the walk was completed were it very warm. Regardless, unless it rained (and the weatherman had predicted a good day) she was going to walk around her Island, warm or cool.

"Her Island". The mere thought of it sent the shivers down her back, and she shifted her small time weathered body under the coverlets. Perhaps it was selfish to think of it this way, so many people had shared it down through the years and even now there were a few fishermen and mossers living in the little cottages both here on the East Side and over on the West Side. The lighthouse keeper, no doubt, thought of it as his Island too. Wasn't he responsible for the safety of the ships passing by and the light and whistle warning of the dangerous shoals around it? But it was her Island, passed on to her by deed, signed by her father and his father before him, along with the heritage come down from those who had settled here more than a century and a half ago.

7

A heritage that when she thought of it, which was frequently, sent the shivers up and down her spine. The bravery and courage of her great great aunt, Mary Hichens, a young maiden brought up in the comparative shelter of a parsonage with all the comforts of a village home, forsaking those conveniences and persuading her husband and brother Edmund to bring a few belongings and sail to his Island and prepare to winter here, facing the bitter storms and cold, to administer to the needs of shipwrecked sailors who might be washed ashore. The stories told by fishermen visiting the Island in the springtime of the bodies washed ashore and evidences that some of those unfortunate men had been alive when they reached land only to freeze to death or die from hunger and exposure had haunted Mary's thoughts and dreams for a long time. When her husband had tried in vain to talk her out of her scheme to move to the Island, she had reminded him that had he been shipwrecked there instead of on an island near the mainland he too might have been counted with the lost.

The courageous families, the Hichens, Crowells, Edmund and his wife Jerusha, and John Nickerson, Jerusha's brother, and wife reached the Island and living in an old fishing shanty as shelter against the wind and cold, gathered wood and stored the crude oil they had brought with them to burn and prepared to spend the winter. Only God knows how they survived those five months before warm spring days came along, or whether He gave them a mild winter or not, but the value of being there to be ready to help those in need impressed the Crowells and Hichens enough that the next summer they built homes, one on the East Side where the Hichens could view the shore and be handy to the South corner of the Island, and the other on the North Side where the Crowells could detect ships approaching the shoals from the Bay of Fundy. The houses were in view of each other and communications were made by lamplight during the long winter nights.

Her heritage. Great grandfather Edmund Crowell, grandfather Corning, uncle Corning Jr. and her father John, ahead of her, responsible for saving the lives of hundreds of men and women alike, washed ashore, warned by the lighthouse built a few years after the brave couples had moved to the Island, or rescued by lifeboat crews; but all saved through the courage and bravery of her ancestors.

The muted sound of the fog horn aroused her from her thoughts and then, as if its sound had been a signal for the birds sleeping in the trees around the house and shore, the morning became alive with their singing. This was the prelude to dawn. Nature's clarion call that soon there would be a streak of light along the horizon and the shade of night would be lifted to welcome a new day. Whether she would see the first ray of light as she raised herself to look out over the ocean, or whether the fog still enveloped the shoreline, made little difference to her. The day had begun and this, her 85th birthday, by the grace of God was hers to make of it what she would.

The sun was trying to force its radiance through the cracks in the dark grayish clouds when she opened the back door to let the dogs out. The usual greetings by the two dogs, shut up in the kitchen during the night, for her and her bedroom companion, were over and the high back rocking chair still rocked where Barney the younger male had vacated it when he heard the step on the stairway. Old Maggie, the little spaniel, 18 years old, toothless and stone deaf, wagged her stub of a tail and looked up at her questioning as to what the day might bring forth. Buddy, the largest of the four, silky haired and lovable, who had his own mat at the top of the stairs by her bedroom door pushed Barney aside to get his share of attention, while Donna, privileged to spend the night with her mistress, had kept jumping at the latch trying to lift it, as she frequently was successful in doing, to go outside.

Rushing past her, out into the fenced in back yard, fenced to keep the sheep out of her flower garden and away from the back door, the dogs went on past the little cemetery where six other dogs were buried. Small cement monuments inscribed: Jack 1944-1960; Gypsie 1947-1960; Jessie May 1954-1967; Cindy 1956-1970; Elizabeth 1958-1970; and Susie 1964-1967; marked where the pets, adored and spoiled by her daughter, now reposed. The dogs were the only family her daughter and husband had, there being no children born of their union.

With not more than a casual glance at the skies, but noting that the wind was from the west, by the way the few clothes on the line waved, she closed the door and went back into the kitchen and made a fire in the cookstove. The "Canada" with its warming closets, topped by fancy work with the mirror in the middle, filled with wood to dry out for burning, was probably the most modern furnishing in the kitchen. Surrounded by the rocking chair, an old hair stuffed couch, two straight backed cane seated chairs at the drop leaf table, and the old Captain's chair salvaged from one of the shipwrecks near the Island, the stove shone in its enameled covering and warmed the room as the sticks crackled and a wisp of steam came from the teakettle spout.

A brass based oil lamp on a swinging rack was pushed against the wall between the window and the table and the carved wooden rack on the wall at the end of the table held another lamp, her mother's pride and joy, with a cherub on the base holding the oil tank and chimney above its hand. A treasure indeed. Two books and her Bible, well worn and marked for daily use lay along side. Between the outside wall and the pantry door, hung the calendar distributed by the Sons of Temperance. A framed picture of the Bluenose II hung between the hallway door and the stove. The space behind the stove standing out a foot or so from the wall was packed with wood drying for future use. The door to the storage room where all her canned goods and sundries were stored, separated the stove and couch covered by an old blanket diffusing the odor of the dog that had slept there all night and showing the effects of long usage with worn and torn patches on its side and exposed end. A color photograph of the Seal Island Lighthouse hung on the wall over the couch where all who entered could see. Two worn scatter rugs were on the lineolum covered floor along with the braided rug half exposed from under the stove where little Maggie had slept for the many winters and summers of her life.

The water hot, she poured a cupful and put a slice of brown bread on the toast rack to toast, while the water cooled enough to drink. Her Morman belief prohibited her from drinking coffee or tea, but she maintained that the hot water did her as much good anyway. Spreading a thin coating of the gooseberry jelly, she had made last year, on the toast, she sat down and now carefully scanned the skies as she partook of her

10

moderate breakfast.

The pink hue of the clouds shading the rays of the sun, and the cobwebs here and there on the grass gave an indication of a good day and she signed with relief in anticipation of the hike ahead. It would be an hour at least before she'd be ready to go, but that would give her plenty of time. It was only about a ten mile walk around the shoreline, and with rest stops, it should not take more than five or six hours to make the trek. Of course, should she find a sick lamb or overtake a stray ewe, it would take time to minister to the needs, whether by giving medicine or shearing the wool.

Right now there were hens and dogs to be fed, some grain thrown out for the crippled ewe who had learned to come to the house each day for food and not forced to compete with its healthy companions for grass which had been nibbled close to the ground, lunch to be put up to eat at the North End, and the shears and medicine set out to take with her in case of necessity.

The dogs followed her to the henpens and Barney treed a squirrel, the first of many for the day, as the dozen hens, some older than she remembered, greeted her in anticipation of their grain and clean water. They kept her supplied with enough eggs for her and her daughter and son-in-law at the Lighthouse, and would live out their natural lives unless by some accident one might be fatally injured or a hawk carried one away as had happened early this spring. As with the sheep, none of them would be killed to be used for food. Their by-products were all she expected from them.

Twisting the wooden knob that kept the door of the storage barn closed, she entered the small building where the grain, firewood, coal and sawdust was stored. On the floor overhead, shingles and boards along with grain bags and other odds and ends, had been carefully put away for future use. Scooping up a can of grain she went to the henpen after carefully fastening the door to keep the sheep out, and proceeded to untie the strand of rope with which she had the gate of the henpen tied. Although the hens were allowed to roam freely around the house, she had to pass through the henyard which was now used as their small garden area to get into the henhouse, feed the hens, collect the eggs and lift the hatch door allowing them outside. The garden where small quantities of carrots, beets, lettuce, cabbage and strawberries were planted was bordered by currant bushes all the way around the fenced in area. The gate had to be kept tied at all times to prevent the sheep from eating up all the vegetables.

Behind the henhouse was a huge pile of wood; logs, driftwood, old buoys and crates waiting to be sawed and split for firewood. A stack of split wood waited to be moved into the barn before winter came. Across the path that led to the Lighthouse from her backgard was a good sized raspberry patch where pails of fruit were picked each summer and made into jam. A narrow road between the raspberry bushes and the storage barn allowed room for the tractor to go in with the coal so that it could be thrown in the back window and not have to be carried through the building. Adjacent to the henyard was a small building where her gas refrigerator was housed so that she could keep her foods cold. For some reason, that no one could determine, the temperature inside the refrigerator couldn't seem to be controlled and much of the food was half frozen when she used it.

Making her way back to the house, she passed the tractor shed where the old Farmall was kept out of the weather. The door hung by one hinge and creaked when the strong winds blew. It would probably fall off before her son-in-law got around to fix it, she mused, but it was his tractor and his problem.

Back in the kitchen, the sun rays caught the slight specks of dust that swirled as she closed the door and made a ray of color across the table as she prepared the dogs' breakfast. There was fish she had cooked the evening before and she carefully picked out the bones and mashed the pieces with the contents of Big Boy dog food. Placing the dishes far enough apart around the room to prevent them from scrapping for each other's food, she knelt down beside little Maggie, who though she couldn't hear what was going on, had a keen sense of smell and was wriggling her small body in anticipation of the meal. Mushing the food in her fingers she fed it in small amounts to the dog who gummed it slowly and then swallowed it. By the time half of the food was gone, the other dogs were

12

pushing around her looking for more. Tenderly she pushed them away and each retreated to his or her chair or couch to wait until Maggie finally finished her meal.

The dogs fed, the water pail filled from the well near the back door and the cup and knife washed and put back in the cupboard, she prepared her lunch consisting of two small smoked herring, a slice of bread and two molasses cookies and packed them in an old lard bucket, which if she was fortunate enough to find any wild strawberries would come in handy. She then settled down in the Captain's chair and took the Bible from the shelf. The dogs snoring in contented sleep seemed to provide a fitting accompaniment to her reading from the old familar passages that she had read and reread since childhood. On long winter evenings, she would read books at a time from the Old Testament prophets or the gospels, losing herself in the problems God's servants coped with or the parables Jesus told, but this morning with the walk ahead, she closed the book after reading a chapter and shut her eyes. It semed appropriate that the dogs stopped snoring as she folded her hands and silently prayed. With a spoken "Amen" she rose from the chair and the dogs on the chairs and couch slid to the floor in anticipation of the day's activities. Old Maggie sensing the movement about her crawled out from under the stove and wagged her stub of a tail.

After carefully wrapping her ankles so that the nettles would not scratch the flesh and there might be a reoccurrence of the ulcers she had suffered so terribly with a few summers ago, she put on her old sneakers, (her boots would get too heavy before the trek would be finished) and even though she would get her feet wet, the sneakers were more desirable than the extra weight to carry around. Tying the denim jacket around her waist in case the air would be cool at the North end, she adjusted the shears, the bag containing the two bottles of medicine and her lunch bucket so that they hung loosely from her hip but wouldn't interfere with her walking. Placing her old weathered felt hat on her head, she rolled down her pant legs and started for the front door. She had considered leaving Buddy behind, because he had a tendency to chase the sheep if they should come out of the woods and surprise him suddenly, but wanting all her dogs to share her day with her, she relented and let him go. Closing the door of the kitchen after a quick glance around, she and the dogs walked along the hall to the front door.

The photograph of the Island taken from a helicopter a few years back caught her eye as she let the dogs out ahead of her, and, even though she had decided days ago she would traverse the Island, she stopped and mused over it once more. Here on the East side, she would head toward the South shore, past the sand bar reaching out into the sea, and on to the Lighthouse at the southeast corner. She would proceed to the West side, cross the breakwater where the nettles were so heavy and then go on to the Northern end. It was here that she would probably have her lunch, with the view of Mud and Flat Islands in front of her, and then follow the familar path back over the cliffs to the narrows, and on to home. She had never actually measured the distance around her Island, but approximately four miles long and a mile across at its widest point, she had estimated it to be a ten mile trip all the way around. A cousin had sent her a pedometer a long time back, but she couldn't seem to read it right the first time and had tucked it away somewhere. With a final glance around the hall and up the stairway, and patting the items tied to her waist, she went out onto the porch, locking the door behind her and tucking the key under her blue polka dot handkerchief deep in her pants pocket.

Chapter 2

Barney had already treed his second squirrel for the day and Buddy had disappeared into the woods seeking rabbits. Donna was down by the shore cottage waiting expectantly and little Maggie hugged her heels as she walked down the brightly colored cemented pathway from the house. She and Mary had laid these four by four blocks at convenient times during the past summers so that now the walk was some thirty feet long, with each square painted a different color. Maybe someday the walk would get to the clearing beyond the trees but there was always so much else to do.

Reaching the old life boat long since retired, she rubbed her hand over the prow and memories took her back to her early days when the life saving crews were active. She recalled almost too vividly the wild stormy nights when a ship was floundering at sea, the men in oil clothes, hip boots and sou-westers, pushing the boat out from shore and nearly capsizing as a huge wave caught the boat broadside, and then rowing safely beyond the breakers and out to the shipwrecked crew. In the wintertime, when the ice wall, so high that you couldn't see the ocean from shore, encircled the Island, the women stood on shore breathlessly waiting for the sight of the boat after it had been pushed over the wall and until, with a sigh of relief, they would see it from the hill beyond the breakers headed out to sea. She had seen over seventy half drowned seamen brought safely to shore in this one boat alone during her girlhood and young womanhood, she had helped carry or lead them to one of the many cottages and helped nurse them back to health again. Only two of the rescued men had died, both of pneumonia, after their rescue. One of the lifeboat crew had been swept into the seas the night the *Mascot* was wrecked and his body was never recovered. She remembered Dr. Hichens tell how his father and Uncle William realizing that their fishing boats were not rugged enough for the hazardous task of facing the billowing waves and taking care of shipwrecked men, used the money they had earned fishing and had a lifeboat built to their own design to meet the Island's rugged requirements. The original lifeboat was probably very similar to the one she stood by right now. The effectiveness of the boat was broadcast far and wide and the Royal Humane Society of England, in appreciation of their efforts, sent a set of seven life preservers. The Hichens boys were credited with establishing the first life saving station in Canada on the little Island. Dr. Hichens had not been active as a member of the lifeboat crew but had had the satisfaction of seeing one of his sons as Captain of one of the lifeboad crews prior to motorboats coming into use in the early 1900's when several families lived year round on the Island.

The historical society in Halifax wanted the boat for display at the museum, but she was determined that it would stay here as long as she was alive. She had saved it from destruction where it had been stored in the old boathouse, saw that it was moved to its present position and here it would stay as long as she or it lasted. With the help of Dr. Benjamin Hichens' grandson, who came to visit the Island each year, she had kept it painted and it was an added attraction to people who visited the Island.

Passing the cottage nearest the shore, where guests, including the birdwatchers, visiting the Island stayed for a few days during the summer months, she noticed the woodpile near the back door was pretty well gone. She made a mental note to have Mary haul a load of driftwood over from the West Side one of these days when she had the tractor and cart over from the Lighthouse. She'd chop it up, a few pieces at a time to relax at the end of a day. The three legged sheep darted nervously from the corner of the house where it had been lying in the sun and bleating noisily headed for the flock that was grazing up on the hillside beyond.

Following the old fence that started about five feet from the corner of the house, she approached the first of a set of buildings. Two ewes came rushing out of the door of the first

16

shed where the sheep were rounded up for shearing each summer. The building, used for storage of the wool and Irish moss until it could be shipped across to the mainland, was built when she was a young girl and housed the Island store where families who lived on the Island year round could buy staple goods to keep them supplied between trips to the mainland. She remembered the many times she had spent her few pennies for sticks of peppermint or a sack of anise drops when she had come over from the cottage by the Lighthouse to pick up some sugar or flour Mother needed to finish her cooking. Mr. Perry's store was a standby in case of shortages and was an intregal part of the Island's history. A "Bull Durham" chewing tobacco sign still hung over the doorway.

Between the shore and the wharf were piles of buoys waiting to be sorted and repainted. Crevices in the sandy roadway were evidence of the heavy spring rains when huge rivulets of water had gushed down between the rocks and tree stumps from the hill, making their way around the stones and clumps of moss in pyramids of foam, and on down across the pathway onto the rocks and sand into the sea. Furrows a foot deep and as wide broke the sandy beach into small peninsulas of their own and cans and brush were washed along into the breakers by the rushing stream.

The incoming waves were colored a deep brown as the salt and fresh water mixed together as the breakers roared onto the shore. The sun breaking through the clouds produced irridescent colors on the small stones which had long been buried under the sand and were now exposed as the rushing currents had washed the protective sands away.

Reaching the sluiceway over which the supplies were brought in from the Government ship and where the fishing and mossing boats were hauled up by a motor powered cable, she headed down the slippery planks to the narrow pier stretching out into the water. How many years the present pier had stood she wasn't sure but she remembered the story of the building of the original wharf way back during the first decade the Hichens and Crowells had lived on the Island.

Realizing the need for greater efficiency in taking care of the shipwrecked crews as they were brought ashore, the two men had gone to Halifax and approached the House of

Assembly for funds to erect a suitable wharf. They had been successful in pleading their case and in 1827 funds were appropriated for construction. The original wharf was built the following summer and proved to be a valuable asset to life saving measures.

She remembered it having been repaired with new creosoted timbers set in to replace the weathered original beams and as a youngster had watched as the slip was built along side. With installation of the power cable and the risk of boats pulling alongside, the pier was used more for a buffer against the waves and for fishing by the youngsters and the visitors than for anything else. She had climbed up on its top a countless number of times to look out over the waters toward Clark's Harbour for the first sight of boats coming from the mainland. The desire to crawl along the timber and onto the pier came into her mind but there was too much to do, so she turned and walked back up the ways.

There was no one in the cable and storage shacks at the head of the sluiceway but she could smell the scraps of fish lying around the shack where they had been preparing the pollock for salting and several barrels of fish soaking in brine were lined along the walls of the building. She was disdainful of the carelessness of the fishermen in leaving the scraps and refuse around. She had often commented on the looks of the place and the offensive odors but they had taken little notice of her observations. On occasion, extra high tides or heavy rains would wash the refuse into the sea "God doing what men had no time to do."

One day many years back, she had discovered a yellowed paper tacked to the inside wall of the storage shed which she had taken and kept for future reference. On it was written, under the name William Swim (who she later learned had died in 1891):

Lobster gear

24 barrels bait at $1.00 per bbl.	24.00
1 iron tank 1.00	1.00
3 puncheons 25 cts. each	.75
2 tubs 75 cts. 1 anchor $3.00 Killick $2.00	5.75

18

```
2 Gal. coal tar  20 ct. each .........................40
220 potheads at 2 cts. ............................4.40
rope  $50.00  1 dory $2.00 ..................... 52.00
95 old lobster pots with buoys  16 cts. ..............15.20
34 new pots with heads at 30 cts. .................10.20
34 crates at 25 cts. per crate ......................8.50
1 chain  $3.00 ..................................3.00
```

Total Value $125.20

Beautiful white, purple and pink nettles bordered the pathway between the buildings, lovely to look at but painful when your legs rubbed against them.

Heading up the rise toward the church, she paused at the pile of rocks spread over an area of about 10 square feet, the site of the first house on the Island. Here Richard and Mary Hichens after spending their first winter in 1823 in the shanty, with their fires burning continuously for warmth and to serve as a beacon for those at sea, built their small home. Here, until their family outgrew the house and another was built near the Lighthouse, Mary and Richard kept their lamps burning, nurtured their children and lived on fish caught offshore, meal brought from the mainland and mutton from the sheep transported to the Island for their use for wool and food and also to have food available for those who might be rescued from ships at sea. Somewhere close to the house were the graves of Hichens children who had died here on the Island. Just the pile of rocks, but a hallowed spot.

It was in the autumn of the third year on the Island that Captain Hichens became restless to sail the seas once more, and leaving his wife and the two babies Richard and Mary Jane, went as "ships husband" to South America. He was gone six months and upon his return from his 3000 mile journey made a land fall of his own home, "a most wonderful thing and most talked of".

Continuing her way to the top of the hill she came to the church. The door to the small entry leading into the church proper creaked a little as she pushed it open. A musty odor filled her nostrils as she opened the door into the large room and she sighed audibly as the sun finally breaking through the clouds sent its rays through the colored glass windows and lighted the room in transcendal beauty. She stood in the middle of the room by the pot bellied stove looking toward the pulpit, the large Bible opened on its top, the two organs, one on each side of the raised platform, ready to send forth their sweet melodies at the touch of the fingers and the treading of the bellows. The lamp stands at each front corner of the platform no longer held the oil lamps (someone had taken them as reminders of the past) but the hanging chandelier still held its four lamps out of reach of those standing on the floor beneath it. The light colored panelling put up two years ago through the generosity of a Yarmouth man in his will and the labor of the Crowell brothers, George and Alton, covered the original paper on the walls, and the enameled whiteness of the woodwork offset the colored window panes as the memory of the day the first service was held within her church flooded her mind. Sitting down in one of the rounded back chairs her thoughts took her back to the living room of the old house, a child playing with her toys in the corner while her mother and neighboring women pieced quilts together, knit mittens, caps and socks and did fancy work around the Ottawa heater, to sell at the annual lawn party and supper each spring to raise money to build a church. For years her mother had dreamed of having their own church on the hill overlooking the East shore, a place of worship where the Islanders could gather together in a building set aside for worship, rather than meet each week in one home or another. Her enthusiasm had spread among the women and as the funds swelled they worked diligently toward their goal. And the dream came true, or as her mother stated following the dedication of the building, "We had faith, but faith without works is dead". With the seven hundred dollars that she had frugally put away she hired Isaac Crowell, a builder, to erect the church. With the volunteer help of the men between their regular duties, the building became a reality. It was a rectangular structure thirty-six feet long, twenty-four feet wide and twenty feet tall with one huge auditorium. To the main room was built a small entry six foot square which was the base of the steeple extending to the height of the main building and tapering with hexagonal sides to a point some thirty-five feet above the ground. As the beacon

20

from the Lighthouse swept across the steeple at night, it resembled an arrow pointing toward the heavens showing people the way to God. Four years after completion, it was fully paid for.

The first service was a memorable event with relatives of many of the Island's inhabitants coming from the mainland to join in a service conducted by a minister from Centreville, Cape Sable Island. The choir made up of the rugged fishermen and their wives rendered several old hymns and the notes of the organ wafted far out across the waves as "Let The Lower Lights Be Burning, Rescue The Pershing, and Throw Out The Lifeline" and other beloved hymns were sung lustily by the congregation. Mother's eyes were never dry during the entire service. In her diary under the date June 10, 1906, she had written "Mr. Hichens preached at the church Sunday. Used as his text 'God forbid that I should glory save in the cross of Christ'."

In recent years with the Island practically uninhabited except during the summer months, services were only held on occasions when groups from Clark's Harbour journeyed across for a Sunday outing and a visiting pastor would conduct a meeting. An offering plate sitting on the pulpit received contributions to maintain repairs that might be needed.

The bleating of a lamb that had been left behind by the flock brought her back to the present and rising she made her way to the entry.

Closing the door carefully and almost reverently behind her, she started down the slope toward to cove. She paused to straighten the little white cross bolstered up by a pile of small rocks and made a mental note to come over and drive the marker into the ground. She read the inscription - Anne Lindsay - Nov. 1891 - age 28 years, and as always when she stopped here breathed a little prayer in memory of this unfortunate soul whose final resting place was probably never known to those who had watched her sail away on the *Ottawa* from England and home. Mother had told the story several times how she attempted to get information from the ship's master, Captain Dixon, as to whom the woman might be so that relatives might be notified of the stewardess's death, but the Captain refused to reveal whether the young woman had living relatives or not. "She's better off dead," he had retorted when mother had insisted on information, "better well done that she died unbeknown to anyone save you and me," and turned his attention to the remaining members of his crew. They had buried her near the church at mother's request and for almost a century the grave had been appropiately revered. The wooden bucket in the front parlor, rescued from the *Ottawa*, was a constant reminder of the wreck and its sad consequences.

She turned to look up at the steeple of the white church pointing toward the sky, the landmark for those approaching the Island from the West. She had heard people tell that on a clear day they could see the Church with binoculars from the nearest point of the mainland at Shag Harbour, fourteen miles away. She had seen the lights on the shoreline many nights as she had walked around her home, but had never seen the Island from the mainland shore. In fact, her visits away from the Island were so few and far between, that she never thought of trying to see the Island when ashore on business or as on the last crossing, a brief stay in the hospital in Yarmouth when the leg ulcers were so bad. During the hurricane of '66, she had watched apprehensively from the shelter of the trees around her home as the church shook from the gusts and actually was moved off its foundation, but it had withstood the gale and was gently set back in place by gradual pulling by the tractor with the aid of strong fishermen, who although hardly ever darkened the doors of the house of worship, still revered it as a symbol of peace and humility within their hearts.

Walking down the slope leading to the South side, she approached the low area protected from normal seas by the breakwater but flooded occasionally when the high tides came up over the rocks and inundated the land. Dried seaweed, rocks and scum covered the area which once was a settlement for some of the lifeboat crew who built their homes on pilage to protect them from the occasional overflow. Wilson Trefry, Uncle Wilse as he was affectionally called by the children on the Island, lived in one of those homes with his young family before moving to the mainland. Wilson was lifeboat captain

22

when she was small and he fell in love with her Aunt Nancy. Plans were made for their wedding to take place in Barrington and he went ahead to make necessary preparations. She remembered the day that he waited expectantly on the pier at Clark's Harbour to meet his bride-to-be, but could only imagine his reaction when instead of greeting a vibrant young woman, he watched as the men carried the box containing her body onto the pier. Aunt Nancy, her mother's sister, had died of an appendicitis attack while getting ready for her wedding.

Later Uncle Wilse took the great granddaughter of Capt. Richard Hichens, Elizabeth, as his bride and lived in his home on this lowland for several years. He was blind as soon as darkness fell and had to be led around in the night hours by others. Yet he was capable of seeing even the slightest glimmer of light at far distances and proved to be an able lifeboat captain during the years he served. Howard Hichens, his brother-in-law, lived farther back from the shore on a bit higher land near the woods before moving over near the Lighthouse.

In her memories of Seal Island, one of Uncle Wilse's daughters, Hilda, who went to the Island to live at the tender age of five weeks, returning to the mainland in 1898, wrote as follows:

> "Dear to my heart are such little happenings as these -
> Watching the kindly lightkeeper wind the light
>   sending its beams 16 miles over the ocean
> Gathering gull's eggs
> Picking wild flowers in wide variety
> Wonder of wonders—a trip out in the lifeboat on
>   practice days
> Huge platters of baked wild fowl
> Trailing behind the kindly lightkeeper's daughter
>   when she would, after a terrific storm, take a
>   wheelbarrow and gather up for burial the
>   hundreds of birds that had dashed against the
>   light and were killed in their migration flight
> Smoky fungus puffs picked and used to heal cut
>   little fingers

The bl l o o o o o o ohing of the fog horn,
   sometimes weeks on end
Picking cups full of delectable tiny tea-berries and
   "oh" the spruce gum which was so abundant
Cranberries spread over an old boat sail in the
   Lighthouse to dry
I remember the trees nearest the shore being as
   grey crowded skeletons with bare twisted
   limbs, gnarled and terribly beat by incessant
   storms, all so dreary yet holding a certain
   fascination
A cable was laid by cable ships in 1916 or 1917
   bringing telephone communication from the
   mainland. It was run from Shag Harbour to
   Seal Island in late springtime.
The thousands of glistening gulls, stormy petrels
   and various wild ducks abounded. Who was it
   that wrote:
         'The seagull sits above the surge
         Upon a rocky shelf:
         For hours on end he feels no urge
         To exercise himself.

         And then he falls headfirst and flies
         On wings that scarcely beat;
         Trying with long-drawn trailing cries
         To find some food to eat.'

On clear cool nights looking off from the shore all one
         can see are the miles and miles of ocean—and
         the many, many twinkling stars God has hung
         in the sky to dry after the heavy drenching
         storms

On this Island still—
         'The breakfast fires are being lit
         Their smoke ascending high;
         Scores of gulls do daily rise
         Into the morning sky.' "

Picking her way over the stones and the dried seaweed where the high tide had washed them far up on the shore and never returned to carry them out to sea again, she approached her gardens, enclosed by snow fence and partly covered with fish netting to keep the gulls from destroying her crops. Bordered by a row of strawberry rhubarb nearly all the way around, were rows of potatoes, turnips, carrots and beets. Root crops did better than other vegetables and could be stored easily for the winter months without pre-cooking and canning. The rich black loam was almost weed free as a result of the constant attention she gave her garden, "to relax at the end of a day," she explained to visitors who admired the crops. If the rats didn't eat up the potatoes, she would have enough to see her through the winter. There were years though when they seemed to multiply faster than she could keep them controlled with poison and a great share of the crop had to be discarded. This area once had several houses on it but they had been destroyed by time and the changing of the tides down through the years.

The path through the woods where the sheep were run into the pen midway through, was dry for this time of year. On some of her walks this would be the area where she would get her feet wet for the first time, but today she could walk the middle of the path without difficulty. The coolness of the spruce and fir interwoven together as they were dwarfed by the salt blowing in from the sea and deformed from the buffeting of the N.E. gale, chilled her and she momentarily considered putting on the jacket tied about her waist, but seeing the light at the end of the wooded tunnel plodded on resolutely toward the warmth of the sun. Branches were banked along each side of the path to keep the sheep from straying off into the woods, especially during shearing activities.

The tide was more than two-thirds of the way out as she came into the full brightness of the sun. She gazed out at the sand bar reaching its arm out into the sea, its fingers clutching at the rocks which emerged as the waters lowered, turned white as the heat touched them and then were wet again as the waning tide resolutely reached out as if in one final effort to cover them before receding farther along the shore. The rocks extending beyond the sand formed a line far into the water and ocean liners kept up to four miles away from the Island to safely skirt the hidden reef of Blonde Rock some three and one-half miles from shore. Smaller fishing boats were able to safely maneuver in the narrow channel discerned a few hundred yards beyond the end of the sands and at low tide the mossers were able to rake great amounts of Irish moss to ship off to the factories to grind into gluten and eventually into food products.

Memories of the *Jebedee M* flooded her mind. She had recorded in her scrapbook how the fishing boat, registered in Barrington Passage, with only the master Elias Smith and his mate Ronald Symonds aboard, had been capsized by heavy seas at the south end of the Island by the bar. In what was said to be one of the most daring feats of its kind seen on the coast. Carl Atkinson and his mate Herman Atkinson drove their boat in between two big breakers and reached Smith's boat. They rescued Smith but could not locate Symonds. The body of young Ronald was found at low tide and laid in the church. His brother Douglas came for the body the next day. "Sad! Just thought I would tell the story," she had written. "I know Carl Atkinson. This was not the only time he has rescued men from drowning."

In her book of shipwrecks, she had compiled for a permanent record the wrecks and other important happenings on and around the Island. She had listed seventeen ships that had met their waterloo on Blonde Rock, including the *HMS Blonde* for whom the rock had been named, wrecked in 1782, to the cargo vessel *Gold Mine* which struck the rock in 1921 and sank.

Listed among the wrecks were the *St. George* from Portland, Maine with a cargo of 20,000 bushels of wheat, which struck the Rock in a heavy gale in 1869. The ship was completely broken up but the crew of fifty were saved and taken to Barrington Passage on the mainland.

Among her prized possessions was a collection of knives and forks embossed with "Diamond Jubilee" which had been salvaged from the *Assay*, a steamer loaded with Queen Victoria Diamond Jubilee 'stuff' as her father had explained to visitors at the cottage, which went onto the Rock in 1897. The

26

steel ship weighing 3901 tons, built in Belfast and of the English Ellman line, and captained by I. Caruthers, left Liverpool, England March 23rd bound for St. John, New Brunswick with dry goods, carving sets, ets. It struck the Rock on April 4th after a fast trip across the ocean. Piloted to shore by the Seal Island lifeboat, the crew of sixty-three in their small boats were extremely hungry when they reached shore. She remembered how her mother and she had garnered all the food they could around the neighborhood and had baked for hours in order to feed the hungry sailors.

Merchandise was strewn all along the Island's shore. Little English sailor suits for young boys, yards and yards of carpeting, broad cloth, trimmings for ladies apparel, bolts of brocaded satin, dozens of carving sets, sailor blouses for little girls and pleated skirts. All of the women and girls of the Island were the smartest dressed of any around at that time.

The *Assay* stayed on Blonde Rock all summer and broke up when the fall storms came, but not before it had accounted for the wreck of another vessel, the *Gerona* bound from Portland to London with a cargo of cattle and produce. The *Gerona* struck the wreck of the *Assay,* left the rock and drifted halfway to Bon Portage Island and sank. Three hundred cattle and horses perished. The cargo valued at over a quarter of a million dollars was also lost but the entire crew was saved.

She remembered vividly that March night in 1900 when the southwest gale hit the Island with the barometer on 28. The roof went off of the barn and the family stayed up all night in fear that the house itself might be severely damaged. The following day and for several days thereafter, wreckage from what was later determined to be from the ship *Planet Mercury* which had left Portland February 17th bound for Bristol, England, and was never directly heard from again, washed up on the shore. Her father and others surmised that the ship had met disaster on Blonde Rock as had so many ill-fated schooners before it. Only one body, supposedly from the *Planet Mercury* was found, washed ashore at Sanford, Yarmouth County, on the twenty-fifth day of the same month.

Also among her notes, copied from the Record of

Shipping of Yarmouth, N.S. by J. Murray Lawson was the account of the *John Murphy* 1471 tons, George Cosman, master, which sailed from Harve on the 24th day of May 1883 for St. John, N.B. in ballast and went ashore near Split Rock at the South End of the Island on the 20th of June. The crew was saved. Several large holes were knocked in her bottom and she filled with water. A wrecking crew was sent from Yarmouth who stripped her of spars, sails and rigging which were taken to Yarmouth. She was floated on the 20th of August and towed via Yarmouth to St. John where she was placed upon blocks for examination. As the estimated cost of repairs would exceed the value of the ship, she was condemned and sold. She was purchased by E. Lantalum who burned her to procure the metal in her hull.

The *John Murphy* was owned by John Murphy, H. & R. Crosby and the estate of J.V.N. Hatfield. Insured for $8,000 in "Marine", $6,000 in "Oriental", $6,000 in "Commercial", $4,000 in "Halifax" and $6,000 in Providence Washington.

Turning away from the sea, she made her way up toward the trees and the plot fenced in with fish netting in the shadow of the woods. The jonquils and daffodils on the graves of three women washed ashore after the wreck of the *Triumph* off Blonde Rock were just past their full bloom. Planted several years ago by her daughter and herself, they had spread so that now all three graves were nearly completely covered. The sheep apparently didn't relish the plants as food and so they blossomed lavishly early each summer and the green grass made a carpet on the resting place of these three, the only bodies found from the wreck. Mary had made grave stones for each one, inscribed with the date of the wreck and an appropriate Bible verse for future generations to note where the three had been laid away. There was no way of finding out their names or even where they sailed from, the ship having picked up crew and passengers at stops on its way from Europe. Wreckage washed up on the shore included a trunk containing children's clothes, so it was an indication that there were children perhaps of these women, who had perished at sea. The wreckage washed ashore, as well as that later taken

28

from grounded vessels, had to be sorted out and half of all taken, had to be given to the Assessor of Wrecks at Yarmouth. Yet there was plenty to be shared among the Island residents from the many shipwrecks around the Island.

She had heard her father tell the story of the *Triumph* many times. Following the big storm, he, a boy of thirteen, and others had watched as the debris came washing ashore on the tide. Suddenly one of them spotted a body among the crates and loose clothing, and then another, and in a few moments, another. As they neared the shore the men waded out into the surf and dragged them in. All three bodies were naked. His father, coming along just as the three forms were stretched out on the beach, ordered the boy to the house. "No fit sight for any lad to behold", he had commented, "stay with your mother until I come." Reluctantly, her father had returned to the cottage but the memory of the unclothed bodies long remained in his mind. The following day, the lifeboats found wreckage of the ship but no signs of life or any other bodies were discovered. And the story didn't end there. The women were buried far back on the shore and markers put over their graves and soon forgotten in the everyday business of the Island.

It was several years later, when a man from Halifax dug up the graves in hopes of identifying the bodies, that the incredible discovery that one had become petrified, and except for decay on one side of the face, was the same as when laid in the grave. The discovery spread from the Island to the mainland and scores of people came to the Island to see the body almost like stone. There were demands to have it transferred to the mainland but the lighthouse keeper insisted that it be placed in the grave once more and left to rest in peace along side the remains of her companion. And so the three had laid together undisturbed, remembered only by her and Mary to this day.

Chapter 3

Rounding the point carefully circumventing the huge rocks and the nettles around there and passing the rusting boiler from days gone by which have been discarded when the new diesel powered generators had been installed, she came to the fence surrounding the whistle station. Calling the dogs, Donna and Buddy, who were nosing around the seaweed covered rocks and Barney who was barking furiously at his seventh or eighth squirrel of the morning, she swung open the gate. Waiting until they had passed her and were racing toward the Lighthouse keeper's dwelling to greet the two dogs her daughter kept with her, she patted Maggie gently on the backside and after carefully closing the gate, walked up the narrow road leading to the Lighthouse. The whistle house, where the huge diesel powered generators provided energy to keep the light shining and where the Lighthouse keeper and his assistant maintained 10 hour watches each day to check the gadgets, do minor repairs and general maintenance, had been built since she had moved to the little house amongst the trees after her husband's death. Now with modern radar equipment, the Government had ordered the building demolished and soon this would be but a memory.

She walked up the roadway bordered by wild raspberry bushes on one side and stunted trees on the other and approached the modern duplex home, where her daughter Mary and her husband, the assistant lighthouse keeper now lived. She envisioned in place of the new home, her modest dwelling that she came into as a baby and had lived all of her life until her husband had passed away. She had memories of the days when the house had bustled with activity relative to those of any lighthouse keeper's family, but added to perhaps because of the lifesaving station and the fishing community,

30

which combined produced a settlement of three hundred people at one time. It was here she had lived her childhood years, had grown into womanhood taking over the duties of the home during her mother's illness. She and Ellsworth, her husband, had lived with her parents, until it became their own home following her mother and father's death a few years later. It was here that she had bathed the fevered brow of her only son, in whom she had harbored so many treasured dreams, and watched him die. It was here that her husband carried her back to the house, the night the light failed, and the memory of that night filled her mind.

It was midwinter and the bitter cold penetrated through the walls of the little cottage. She and Ellsworth sat near the kitchen stove. While he read, she darned his socks and listened to the wind howling around the corner of the house. Suddenly her husband looked up and jumped to his feet. "Something's happened! the light's not burning," he fairly shouted and grabbing his jacket raced through the doorway toward the Lighthouse. Wrapping her heavy sweater around her, she followed him into the yard and looking up saw the stationary light beaming out across the seas. "At least the whistle's blowing," she thought as the blast of the steam powered horns rasped in her ears. Entering the Lighthouse, she could hear her husband hustling about on the higher level. Mounting the steps, she saw him working feverishly at the wheel that held the cable which turned the lamp around. "The cable's snapped. We'll have to turn the light by hand," he explained as she reached his side and he looked up into her anxious eyes. "I'll go to the top and get the table moving again. Get me the lamp so I can warm my hands if they get cold."

Rushing back to the cottage she fetched the lantern and climbed the steps to the top once more. Ignoring his orders to return to the house, she sat there beside him shivering with the cold while she watched him laboriously turn the heavy table by hand. "He will be exhausted by morning," she thought, "oh if daylight would come soon." She had dozed momentarily, partially numbed by the cold, and mostly because she just couldn't keep her eyes open, when she heard his sharp exclamation. "The whistle's stopped! I'll have to go and get it going again." He looked her full in the eyes. "Can you keep the light turning?" he asked anxiously.

"I'll keep it turning, I've done it before. Go!" Bracing her hands against the table she started it moving around once more as Ellsworth descended the stairs and she heard the door slam as he went out of doors. Time and time again, it seemed as if she could not exert any more strength to keep the light moving but with a prayer on her lips she pushed and pushed and the rays revolved out across the waves.

The first ray of daylight began to show on the horizon before she ever thought of slowing her pace, and the whistle had not yet sounded. Anxiety welled within her and finally, deciding that it was light enough, she left her post, descended the stairs and raced towards the whistle house. Passing the cottage, she headed toward the shore unmindful of the darkness between the trees and the roots that protruded on the pathway. Catching her toe on a root, she hurtled to the ground, striking her head sharply, and everything went black.

She awoke lying on the couch in the kitchen, Ellsworth applying a wet cloth to her head and praying audibly for God's help. As her eyes opened, he gave vent to his feelings and his tears wet her cheeks as he kissed her time and time again. "The light—the whistle?" she queried, trying to rise and feeling a wave of nausea as she lifted her head.

"Everything's all right dear, the whistle's blowing and it's bright enough outside now, it's you I'm—"

"I don't know what happened I —"

He interrupted her, "Tripped on a root I imagine. Almost fell over you coming up the path when I realized the light wasn't turning. Thought something had happened to you. Why did you leave it?"

Tears welled in her eyes. "I'm sorry! I just didn't know what was happening down at the whistle house, I——"

"Everything's fine now, you just lie back and rest. You're sure you're all right?" The tone of his voice expressed his deep concern.

"Just a bump," she replied, gingerly touching her head, "I'll be up getting breakfast in a few minutes. I'm sorry I—" Weariness possessed her and she closed her eyes and drifted into sleep feeling the strength of his hands holding hers. All was well.

It was here, as she had noted in her scrap book that she had entertained visitors to the Island—"some famous, all important". Thoughts of that glorious summer day in 1917 when she was helping with the family wash and heard voices in the yard, came to her mind. She remembered going out on the porch and meeting the crew of fishermen in their oil suits, among them her Uncle Sylvanus from Wood's Harbour.

"Where in the world did you come from?" She gazed into the wan faces of the men. "Sunk!" was her uncle's reply. "Sunk by that damn submarine."

She had looked at him increduously, having never heard him speak in that tone of voice or using that kind of language.

"Where's your father," Uncle Sylvanus inquired.

"He's on the East side, but come into the house and have something cold to drink," she invited and the men followed her inside.

Later on, after her father had returned from the slip, they told their story.

"We were out there fishing," Uncle Sylvanus explained, "just got our lines over this morning when a shot rang out. Didn't see a thing, and then a second shot went between the two masts. Out of the sea, a submarine came up beside us and a burly sailor ordered us to get into our dories and get away. 'We're sinking your boat.' Another, whom I presume to be the Captain, said in broken English, 'Hate to do this but it's orders,' he continued, holding up flags from different vessels he had torpedoed. Looking at his compass he pointed toward the Island here. He allowed us some food and we took off for shore without asking any questions. I'm sure that he meant business. Didn't even look back. I didn't care to see my vessel destroyed."

Hardly had Uncle Sylvanus finished his story when the sound of voices reached their ears. Going outside, they met the crews of two other boats walking up the pathway. With sixty men to feed, all other plans that had been made for the day were forgotten.

And the sinking of Uncle Sylvanus' vessel was

33

duplicated during the Second World War when in 1942 the Liverpool packet, Norman Smith, master, was torpedoed and sunk by a German U boat. One man of the crew was killed but the rest of the crew landed safely on the Island in their own dories on a beautiful clear Sunday morning so like the day twenty-five years earlier when the fishermen had arrived.

At a later date during the war, a sixty-one year old Captain who had commanded vessels during the first world war, saw his ship go down with flags flying after an attack by a German submarine, adjacent to the Island. It was early evening in the spring, one lifeboat was smashed and two men perished. The others crowded quickly into the only other boat and rowed toward shore. It took twenty-one hours to reach the Island guided by the beams of the light. The Captain and his seventeen surviving crewmen were taken by fishermen to the mainland the following day.

Mary came out onto the back steps and the dogs gathered around her jumping in joyful reunion, lapping her face and responding to her gentle fondling. "Come in," she said, but her mother anxious to continue to walk said she had wasted too much time already, pausing here and there recalling the past, and politely refusing the invitation started on toward the shore leading to the West side. "You be careful," Mary called after her as she walked away.

The reflection of the huge lamp in the top of the Lighthouse catching the rays of the sun cast interesting shadows on her as she walked along and she recalled the history of the erecting of the lighthouse as passed down from generation to generation, recorded in the history of Seal Island and the records of Barrington, the parent township from whence the original settlers of Seal Island came.

It was Mary Hichens who, not content with the work she, her husband and cousin's family were doing in saving lives of shipwrecked sailors, insisted that a lighthouse be built to warn ships at sea of the dangers of Blonde Rock and other shoals nearby. After several attempts to convince the Canadian government that a lighthouse was necessary, she succeeded in persuading Sir James Kempt, Governor of Nova Scotia, to spend some time on the Island, and he surveyed for a suitable spot to build a lighthouse. The highest point on the

Island bears his name but the lighthouse was erected nearer the shore. The House of Assembly voted a thousand pounds to build the structure with New Brunswick paying half the cost as vessels bound in and out of the Bay of Fundy would be benefitted.

A man named Cameron, an honest worker, was hired as builder and massive sixteen inch square timbers were towed across the waters to the Island, dragged from the East side through the woods to the southern point and fitly framed together to make forty seven foot lengths. The timbers were set on a rock and mortar foundation four foot high at corners of the eight sided building, so erected to present the least resistance to winds which came from every direction. Through skilful manipulation they were kept upright while fitted together and reinforced with heavy natural growth knees. Six steps in the foundation led up to the wooden structure. The structure itself was octagonal with eight sides approximately thirteen feet wide. The sixteen inch timbers were supported at each joint by six struts attached to eight by twelve cross beams. The first floor area was ten and a quarter foot high with a thirteen step stairway to the second landing. A sixteen inch square center box was built up the middle of the wooden frame.

The second floor found the corner posts centered nine foot nine inches from their centers with another thirteen steps built along one side of the octagon leading to the third landing. Tapering toward the top, the corner posts were eight foot four inches from center to center at third floor level. Whereas the height of the first and second rooms were the same, the space between the third and fourth floor was two inches lower with eleven steps leading up along the wall of the fourth floor. Here the corner posts were seven foot between at centers and nine foot five inches from the floor to ceiling. Another twelve steps went up to the fifth landing again following the adjacent wall of the octagon toward the top.

The height between the fifth and sixth floors was seven foot eight inches with the sixth floor supported by naturally formed knees cut from the trees. The corner posts were now tapered in so that they were five foot eight inches apart center to center. Eleven steps led to the sixth floor level.

The two inch thick flooring was supported by nine and a quarter by three inch beams with staggered widths ranging from eighteen inches to twenty-four inches between them on all floors to the sixth. The top floor was laid on beams spanned twenty-one inches apart.

The sixteen inch wide posts supported the sixth floor which was round, compared to the octagonal shape of the other floors. Set on this wooden base was a steel cylinder nine foot nine inches in diameter and seven foot high. The original light mounted on this base stood another nine foot high so that the top of the lighthouse was sixty-seven feet above the ground. Cut into the steel cylinder was a three by five foot door opening out on to a catwalk built around the entire cylinder. The walk, three foot ten inches wide, was enclosed by a three and one-half foot high railing built with hexagonal corners eight foot apart.

A ten foot iron curved ladder led up to the base of the revolving light with a twenty inch apron at the top of the cylinder overlapping the catwalk.

Built on an elevation thirty-five feet above sea level, the light sent its beams up to sixteen miles across the waters. The structure was shingled when built in 1829 and reshingled in 1902 when the light cylinder was replaced.

The light was a fixed light for seventy-one years with cups of seal oil set on a heavy cast iron table burning through a five wick cone. The wheel was turned by crank on the next lower level and required a man on duty at all times to keep the table revolving. The building was started in 1827 by Mr. Cameron who in his spare time built a little cottage, the first real cottage on the Island. The light first shone on November 28th, 1831. While Richard turned the crank sending the warning rays across the sea, his wife gave birth to his first daughter, Sarah, the first baby born on the Island.

Captain Hichens and Edmund Crowell alternated in keeping the light, six months at a time, and were paid thirty pounds a year by the Canadian government. Out of this sum, they bought or built boats for rescue work and for their own business of fishing. After Captain Hichens returned to sea again, Mr. Crowell took over complete supervision until his son replaced him, who in turn was succeeded by his son. When the third Crowell died his brother John kept the light for twenty-six years succeeded by his son-in-law Ellsworth Hamilton who was keeper for sixteen years. Then for the first time a lighthouse keeper, not related to the Hichens-Crowell family took over the lighthouse keeping duties. In succession following Ellsworth Hamilton were Lewis Spinney 1941-1946, Edward Gallant 1946-1950, Elijah Jeffrey 1950-1951, Bradford Flemming 1951-1973. (Maurice Swim served as lighthouse keeper 1973-1977, followed by her son-in-law Jimmy Nickerson in 1977-1978 and Raymond Tiner serving from 1978 to present writing.)

She remembered the excitement that prevailed that day in 1902 when the new light, installed at the top of the wooden structure, spread its rays across the ocean waves. It was a revolving lamp with three flashes made by a French inventor and imported here to the Island. It had taken several days to built the wooden framework up the side of the Lighthouse structure with a runway constructed well away from the walls so that the iron castings would not scrape the sides of the building, as they were eased up the runway to the top by ropes pulled by four teams of oxen on the opposite side of the lighthouse. As each section was drawn slowly up the framework, the suspense mounted. Fears were experienced by everyone, except the man who had constructed the frame, that the ropes might break or the iron section slip over the side. Each section was bolted to the base at the top of the main structure as soon as it was set in place and then to the adjointing section to prevent any bumping by the next section to be drawn up.

There was also the fear that ships at sea, missing the friendly rays might founder on the shoals. Long hours were spent in getting the old light frame down, a task as slow and tedious as getting the new one up and in place. But the job was completed with no mishaps and God blessed their efforts by providing clear calm days and nights wherein to work. The light had been changed from a five wick lamp to a French vapor light in 1892 and remained as a vapor light in the new frame until converted to electricity in 1959. Somewhere among her possessions were the glass plate photos of a section being drawn up into place on the wooden framework.*

*In 1978, the light was changed once again with the old iron three flash frame replaced by a wooden six sided two flash frame. The old frame and light were removed in sections and stored away to be later placed at Barrington Head as a historical monument and museum.

Looking up to the top of the Lighthouse, she realized that she could spend the whole day here reminiscing on the many things that had happened around this beacon as it sent its beams across the seas. There had been so many serious events, yet many delightful soul satisfying occurrences that brought peace to a troubled soul. In her mind's eye she once again lay on the green lawn, kept short by the sheep's consistent nibbling, looking up into a starlit sky watching the sweep of the light and hearing the deep but tender voice of Dr. Hichens as he walked the catwalk below the beacon singing hymns out into the night air. She often had wondered why he would climb those many steps to the top of the Lighthouse to do his singing but never had the courage to ask him. Perhaps, she thought, he felt a real nearness to God, getting as close to Heaven as he could get on the Island, and singing his hymns of praise to his Lord. His closeness to his creator showed in his daily life and in the faith that all who knew him had in his counsel and wisdom. He was certainly one, she felt, who practiced what he preached.

During the fifteen years from 1902 to 1917, her father who was then lighthouse keeper did not have a vacation nor did he miss a single watch assigned him on the light and steam fog alarm which had been installed. He could not find a man to relieve him because of the vapor light being so difficult to maintain. She remembered how exhausted he used to get trying to accomplish the things that had to be done during the hours that he was off duty and then taking his own watch.

She recalled the time she watched him hauling the wood he had cut for fuel to heat the water for steam from the pond a half mile distant from the house. He actually slept by laying his head on his hands folded on the tailboard of the wagon as he walked back and forth, not having laid down to rest for six days. The oxen were so exhausted when the hauling was finished that they had just stood in their tracks when the yoke was finally removed.

How vivid were the memories of that last day in January 1973 when the winds reached a velocity of almost seventy miles an hour and a large section blew out of the side of the Lighthouse. There had been rumors that the building might be torn down, as were several lighthouses along the

Nova Scotia shoreline, now that radar was being utilized for warning vessels at sea, and she felt deeply inside that this disaster would convince the Government officials to dismantle her light. Her fears were confirmed when men came to repair the structure the following month and then after surveying the damage recommended that the building be torn down rather than repaired. Miraculously, the decision was reversed and the side was reinstalled and the Lighthouse shingled and repainted bright red and white once more. She had knelt by her bed and thanked the Lord for keeping her light intact.

It seemed unrelated to her thoughts about the Lighthouse, but perhaps because it occurred the same year as the miraacle of rebuilding took place, that she remembered the fall of '73 when the Clark's Harbour postmaster came and closed down the Seal Island post office (which actually was a shelf in her kitchen) and took all the equipment, stamps, postmark stamper and bags away. Expressing her disappointment in her scrap book, she had written "It is quite a blow to us all. You know what mail means—we have gone back to the dark ages." Since that time, she and the lighthouse keepers depended on fishermen to pick up their mail at Clark's Harbour and deliver it to them when convenient. The lighthouse keeper's cheques were delivered by helicopter, however, once a month.

With these many memories, she started on her way once more passing the spot where a little house had once stood. It had last been used as a storage building, but she remembered the yarn that she had heard repeated several times about the engineer for whom it had been built when they put in the first steam alarm in 1870. The man who planned the house was hanged in Halifax for the murder of Sarah Margaret Vail some time after 1870. She couldn't recall the engineer's name only that he was the only one ever sent from Halifax. The lighkeeper took charge of the fog alarm as well in April 1873.

Chapter 4

Passing through the gateway of the fence surrounding the Lighthouse yard, she headed for the shore and the West side. The breakwater had fashioned a fairly good sized pond which had been named Ship's Pond ever since a ship loaded with coal took fire and came ashore with a full crew. Finding no shelter from the bitter cold, the crew perished and their bodies were found lying by the pond the following spring. As other areas of the Island took their names from various happenings or families associated with that area, so Ship's Pond took its name from the unidentified vessel which had come aground. The pond froze over solid in the winter and provided recreational facilities for the youngsters on the Island.

It was on Ship's Pond that she had learned to skate on her Hans Brinker skates fastened to her shoes by worn straps and fishnet cords. Her father had her on skates by the time she was three years old and because the older children did not want to spend their time teaching her and picking her up all of the time, he provided her with an old chair for her to push in front of her for support and a feeling of security as the others skated merrily around her. At the end of the skating period, he would come after her and carry her home on the chair.

Skirting the pond, she started her trek across the heath probably the most monotonous portion of her hike. She was forced to move down onto the rocks in several places as the ground was so swampy she could sink to her knees in spots. Her only respite from the wet area was when she walked over Green Head, the one high spot between the Lighthouse and the West side.

Green Head always had its memories as being the site of the first wreck to occur after she had been born. In 1890, when she was not quite a year old, the *Henry Burnham,* a 473 ton vessel built in Boston in 1873 and bound from New York to Halifax struck just north of Green Head with its cargo of 200 tons of hard coal. She was a total wreck. Some thirty-two years later, the *Sanstad,* loaded with sugar, struck near the same spot. The Captain put anchors over and hauled her off. Proceeding on to Halifax, she was overhauled and over one hundred fifty plates were reset in drydock.

In her book, written among her many other anecdotes, was the story passed down among the Islanders about James Symonds, father of Thomas, who lived at the light station with Corning Crowell, Sr. when he was keeper from 1855 to 1870. Jamie, as he was called, was very smart and active. A ship was ashore up to Green Head and grandfather Crowell was up to the ship. The Captain did not have a man who could get to the top mast head to put a rope through the block, which was what he wanted to do.

Grandfather said, "I've got a boy who can do it in the twinkling of an eye." The Captain sent for him and James Symonds did it "in the twinkling of an eye". In her collection of photographs, she had a picture of James Symonds sitting on the Lighthouse steps surrounded by his grandchildren.

Carefully picking her way along, using as a support the sturdy stick she had found near the graves of the three women, she finally approached the settlement at the West Side. Looking out at the sea, she gazed upon Devil's Limb where so many ships had been wrecked, and the Limb beyond.

The first ship recorded in her book wrecked off Devil's Limb was the *Adriann* which struck the Ledge in 1863. In 1876, the *Live Oak* captained by a Mr. Olson, hit the Ledge during a heavy gale. The Captain's wife refused to take her baby and leave the ship at the request of the Seal Island rescuers. She was taken by force by the able rescuers and saved along with the crew. The *Mascot* struck Devil's Limb in 1901 and she remembered watching the ship break up as she stood on the catwalk of the Lighthouse. Its entire crew survived. In 1929, the *Guard of Halifax* was salvaging the *Snipe* which had been wrecked on Black Ledge when it struck Devil's Limb and was a total loss.

It was here, also, that the *Whiteway*, 299 ton, of Parrsboro, Nova Scotia, met its end in 1934. She could remember going aboard with the "gang" and salvaging boards and hard coal.

Out some two miles beyond lay Black Ledge itself, a flat topped rock where vegetation had once flourished. Back when it had been granted to her father and uncle by the Canadian Government, it had been covered by an acre of turf and garnets nested there in large numbers. They had perhaps dreamed of putting a beacon light on its grassy shoals but since the early 1900's it was baretopped, the silent possessor of a half hundred ships that had met disaster on its jagged edges which glistened in the sunlight as the tides receded. It had received its name from the master of Her Majesty's pride of the ocean the *H.M.S. Blonde*, and would be recorded as part of Seal Island, the elbow to the Bay of Fundy, being the point where the Atlantic Ocean began and the Bay of Fundy ended. The Island itself had received its name from Samuel Champlain when he landed amongst the hundreds of seals loafing around this same West Side back in 1604.

In her collection of articles, obtained from the various wrecks around the Island, was a platter which her grandfather had saved from the *Columbia* the Royal Mail ship bound from Boston to Liverpool via Halifax with mail and ninety passengers. Striking Black Ledge back in 1842, this was the first Cunard line ship to be wrecked off the Island. Fortunately, due to the quick action of the Island men, the passengers and crew were saved.

Four years later the *William Abrams*, a full rigged ship of 706 ton bound from Boston to Calcutta, struck Black Ledge. The Captain, James Hamlin, first knew where he was when he discovered the wreckage of the *Columbia* nearby.

Clear in her memory was the day in 1923 when her father spotted a ship foundering near the Ledge from his lighthouse observation point. Before the lifeboat had reached her, the *Aberdeen* a government supply ship loaded with

42

material for Cape Sable Lighthouse, the crew was on their way toward shore in their dories. An immediate call for assistance went to Halifax and before the vessel broke up in the pounding waves, the cargo had been safely removed. In her album of picture memories was included the photograph of the *Aberdeen* and the *Snipe* an American registered ship that had struck the Ledge a few days earlier, as they lay together gradually being pounded apart by the heavy seas.

Nearby was Scratchall, a smaller expanse of ledge which held claim to being the site of the wreck of the *Orinco* in 1907. This vessel of 1550 ton met disaster on July 26, 1907 when it was stranded on Scratchall on its trip to England. The entire crew was saved but the ship and cargo was a total loss.

Even farther out in the ocean was Elbow Ledge which itself held claim in its own right of having been the site of several wrecks down through the years. Clear in her memory was that day in July 1942, when shortly after being alerted by the keeper of the light on Bon Portage, that several German U boats were in the vicinity, the *William McClay*, an American vessel, became stranded on Elbow Ledge. Loaded with munitions of war and bound for overseas, she had been chased out of the convoy by one of the German submarines. Apparently the U boat had not followed up its advantage in separating the ship from the convoy and other ships came and took the cargo off board until she was lightened enough to float off the ledge. The *William McClay* was taken to Pubnico, pitched, and put back into service in a short time.

Here at the West Side, she found a crate with the initials C.S.I. painted on its side (Cape Sable Island) and sat down on it to rest. The driftwood, stumps of trees uprooted from the surrounding islands and from the mainland, lobster traps, crates, buoys and timbers from old wreckage or discarded boats from the shore, were washed high up on the rocks and here frequently her daughter would come with her tractor and haul loads of wood back for winter burning. Occasionally, they would find uniquely shaped pieces of driftwood like the short branch, tapered at both ends with a knothole in the center, that she had given to a cousin who had visited with her on the Island. He had written that he had polished and varnished it and inserted a small clock in the knothole making a splendid mantle showpiece. They had found other odd shaped pieces, resembling birds or fish and the like.

She looked out on the rolling surf for a short time and then calling to the dogs who had wandered down over the rocks, except for little Maggie who lay by her feet, she made her way between the fishing cottages. Only half a dozen of them were now used by fishermen who came for a week or more at a time to salt their pollock and cod, or to haul their boats high up on the slip to scrape and repaint them. The other half dozen houses in ruins and various stages of decay sat dark and empty, birds flying in and out through the broken window panes; the shingles scattered on the ground where they had been ripped off the roof or sides by the relentless gales. The long sharply slanted roofs nearly came within reaching distance from the ground so that the snow would melt off quickly. Stark reminders of a past when some fifty families lived here on the West Side year around, the walls and outhouses long abandoned and the little storage shacks where the lobster buoys, floats and gear falling in amongst the rubble that had been left behind. Visitors to the Island had taken most of the net covered glass floats and bobbers as souveniers, having been replaced for use by the fishermen by plastic or cork floats.

The house that Edmund Crowell built when he had moved from his original home at the North End and later occupied by Ben Hichens had fallen or been torn down, but the skeleton of the barn where Dr. Ben had bravely fought off members of the gang called Finians' Raiders still stood. The account of his relentless and courageous stand against these pirates of the sea and the islands surrounded the coast had been passed on to each generation of families from those who had lived on the Island at that time.

Spotting the raider's vessel off shore, John Crowell had spread the alarm to the few women in their homes and then raced to the Lighthouse to warn his own family. Gathering a few precious belongings, the Crowells, Thomases and others hid in Wizard's Glen surrounded by dense forest and rocks. Meanwhile Captain Ben had driven his horse and cow into the barn where he was trapped when the Finians landed. Grabbing

44

an iron bar, he ascended to the loft and there challenged the men entering the barn. How long he fended them off or with what weapons they might have used against him, no one had ever seemed to recall to mind. After awhile the raiders left taking Ben's dog and a barrel of salt pork with them. As modest as he was, Captain Hichens seldom related his harrowing experience to anyone but the Finians were never seen near the Island again although they were active in other areas, so active in fact, that the Canadian government, many years later, paid victims of the raiders for losses incurred.

Adjacent to the barn had stood the lifeboat house down by the shore, lone since razed, and just beyond still stood the large house built by her father and uncle of lumber brought from the wreck of the *Samuel Welch* which met it demise in 1886.

She could name the many families that had come and gone since she was a girl, the chums she had gone to school with at the little one room school between the church and the lighthouse where Miss Daisy had taught for some 26 years preceded and succeeded by others who had stayed for a year or two and then gone on to other more populated schools on the mainland. Some of these came back once in a while for a picnic or just a trip over with one of the lobstermen and called in to reminisce with her over a cup of tea and a slice of her Washington pie that she always had available. There were the Nickersons, the Lewises, the Thomases (her mother had been a Thomas) the Crowells, Smiths, Jones, Kenneys, Knowles, Christies and other names well established in Nova Scotia and Cape Cod, Mass. where many of the families had originated as descendants of the early Pilgrims landing in Plymouth.

Just beyond the last house now standing, one of the largest, with its eastside roof coming down to within eight feet of the ground was the site of the lobster factory built in the fall of 1914. This two storey building approximately fifty feet long and twenty feet wide housed a thriving business for a few years. Lobsters, nine inches and over, were shipped to Yarmouth by the *Wanda, Hugh D* and other boats, then on to Boston. Each man shipped his lobsters in his own name and was paid by check from the Boston dealers. All smaller than nine inches were sold to the Island factory which also had a store. Mr.

Leslie Wilson of Barrington Passage was store keeper, assisted by his daughter Ruth, as clerk. Jeffrey Messinger was cook. Mr. Bethel from Port Latour was in charge of the factory and many girls from Pubnico were employed during and shortly following the lobster season.

She couldn't remember just how many years the factory was in operation, but apparently it did not prove satisfactory or with the power boats coming into use, it was found more convenient to take the lobsters directly to the mainland or Cape Sable Island for processing, because operations ceased and the building was torn down by Philip Jones and his sons. The grass had grown up where it once stood and the only tangible reminder she had was the photograph in her collection of treasured pictures.

The *Hugh D* also carried other cargo besides lobsters. In the old days, as she termed them, it brought huge trunks of dry goods from a Montreal clothing store. Mr. Albert Holms accompanied the trunks, sold the goods, and then returned to Yarmouth for another load. Men's suits sold for $4.90, some of them worth $8.00 or $9.00.

The cement pier, which had been built only a few years back in 1960, had cracked in several places and great gaps continually widened as the tide gradually washed the sand and stones away and the ice expanded and forced the splits wider with each freeze. It had been rumored that men were being sent over to rebuild the pier this summer but if it were like other projects, it would be two or three years before they would arrive and the pier would probably have fallen into the sea by that time. How they moved the huge sections of cement she would be interested in seeing when the time came.

Along side the pier was the wide slip, timbers with two by fours about a foot and one half apart, nailed across them, starting well out into the water at low tide and built on a gradual rise some one hundred yards up on the shore, so that the small fishing boats and skiffs, and even the larger Cape Island boats could be pulled up out of the sea even at high tide. She was fascinated the day Ronnie Kenney came up to the slip with a rack truck aboard and drove it off of the planks that it had ridden on from the mainland onto the slip and on up to the shore.

At the top of the slip was the small engine house where the pulleys attached to the engine hauled the boats up over the slip, much simpler she reasoned that when the fishermen used to haul their boats by tugging and pushing. Alongside were piled lobster traps, fishing gear, netting to be repaired for the next season's lobster fishing and flat stones for weighting down the pots. Bags of Irish moss waiting to be hauled to the processing plants at Shag Harbour and Pubnico were piled on the slip below high water so that the tides would keep them soaked down.

She walked carefully around the Cape Island boat, half turned on its side, and scrutinized the paint job that was half finished. It was early in the year to see a boat on the slip being refinished. Most of the fishermen waited until late August and early September when there was a greater chance for bright sunny days. The paint would dry much more rapidly at that time than in the early summer when the fog persisted until midday and then came rolling in again in the late afternoon. She could make out the letters *Sally Ann — Barrington* which had been painted over the white paint but would be relettered in bright blue before the boat went back into the water again.

Chapter 5

The West Shore connected with a long rock laden breakwater over which the high seas sometimes washed leaving a salt water pond on the lee side where gulls, wild ducks and even the ten domestic ducks raised by one or two of the fishermen flocked together to swim and feed. She spied a white duck with seven little yellow ducklings swimming happily together and shuddered at the realization that the little ones would be snapped up by the gulls, perhaps before the day was out. Both the domestic and wild ducklings hardly ever survived to reach maturity unless rescued by a fisherman and kept enclosed while growing up. The pond had once been used for lobster storage while the factory was in use before the pounds had been established at West Head and the Hawk on Cape Sable but that had been long ago. Someday, she thought, heavy seas driven by hurricane winds would probably wash out some of the breakwater and with the seas rolling in might cut the Island in two. The bank from the Northern End to the East Side had been gradually washing out even in her lifetime making the strip between the West Side and Hichens Cove ever narrower.

It was slow, difficult walking over the rocks of the breakwater. Nettles had forced their way between the stones on the lower sides and a loose stone could cause a bad fall. Traps, buoys, shells, and skeletons of trees on the rocks added to the difficult walk. Tediously she made her way along the ridge and finally had covered the three hundred or more yards to the land. Pushing the rushes away she headed for the shambles of the old house standing on the rise safely above high tides. The stones of the foundation were still in place. The weather beaten boards were broken in places and huge cracks

48

where they had split let the winds and rains in. The windows had long been broken out but the frame was still solid, a memorial to those who had lived there during years past. It was near here that Edmund Crowell had built his shelter the first year he had come to Seal Island, at the pleading of his sister Mary Hichens, with his wife leaving their three young children in Barrington. From this North Side they could warn the ships away from Devils Limb and other shoals and also see the glow of the Hichens flares on the East shore. As she sat there on the rock her thoughts reviewed the history of the events transpiring when Edmund and his wife left their three children ages 12, 9 and 7 and returned to the mainland for supplies that November morning, the year following their first visit to the Island.

Mary and Richard Hichens had returned to Barrington a couple of days previous for the birth of their child, her mother having insisted that the baby be born where the best care could be given it. The Crowells knowing that supplies would be needed to last out the winter, reluctantly left their children, promising to return the following day. But the next day, an unexpected storm had blown up and the parents were unable to leave the mainland for the Island. Then storms and off shore winds followed in succession and winter set in. In desperation, they made several attempts, as did others, to reach the Island fourteen miles away but the winds made them turn back. What had happened? What would happen? Their anxiety for their children mounted day in and day out.

It wasn't until early April that they finally were successful in reaching the Island. Expecting to find the bodies of their children, perhaps frozen to death or having died from starvation, they were overwhelmed to find the three of them, somewhat thinner than when they had left them behind the previous fall, but alive and well after their winter's experience. All right as far as food, seal oil and tinder box for heat and light were concerned, the youngsters had not grown anxious or disturbed for several days after their parents had left them behind. Then when the realization that they might never return dawned upon them, they with the courage that had been passed on to them by their parents and ancestors, prepared for the worst.

49

Under the supervision of their sister, the boys gathered wood to keep the fires going for warmth. They shot ducks and crows, and with their meager supply of potatoes, grown the previous summer, kept from starving. As spring approached and the days grew longer, their existence became more sure, and although they experienced bitter winds and cold nights, none of them caught severe colds or became ill. They feared that their parents had drowned attempting to return to the Island, but the reliance on God taught them by their father fully sustained them. "We'll be all right, God is with us, they will come back,"the boys had been reminded time after time by their sister, and their trust in her confidence kept them going day after day. What a joyful reunion took place that April day.

It was the light from this original house that the crew of the *Vivid* saw when they thought that they were doomed to die on this forsaken Island. At night, and in a blinding snow storm, the vessel had run high up onto Race Point at the northern end of the Island. The half frozen seamen had all managed to get safely ashore after hanging to the jib-boom and crawled amongst the scrub trees for shelter, wondering as to what would happen to them on this supposedly uninhabited Isle. Half paralyzed with the cold and thoroughly exhausted, three or four crawled away from their companions and discovered what seemed to be a trail through the woods. Painstakingly they crawled on hand and knees under the snow laden branches and suddenly saw a light coming from the candle in the window of Edmund Crowell's home. Half running, half crawling, they managed to reach the door and with quivering lips told their story. Edmund Crowell signalled the disaster sign to the Hichens who saw it from their East side dwelling and together the two men went out into the stormy night, and while their wives ministered to the needs of the men who had spread the alarm, found the remaining seamen, who unbelievingly followed them back to warmth and shelter. Had it not been for that candle light in the window, the crew of the *Vivid* would probably have succumbed as had so many unfortunate seamen before them. With an average of a wreck a year on or near the Island in the several years that followed, not one sailor ever escaped the ruins of his ship, only to reach the

50

Island and die because assistance was not at hand.

Adjacent to the decaying house stood another two storey dwelling built by John and Croning Crowell of lumber they brought from the wreck of the *Samuel Welch* which was destroyed in 1886. In fairly good condition, the house was now occupied by groups of birdwatchers who visited the Island frequently to study the many species that inhabited the Island or used it as a resting place on their migrations south and north each year.

Travelling was much easier along the path toward the North End and Race Point. Occasionally she would have to go in around the low hanging branches of the trees where the edges of the bank had been washed away, but most of the time she was able to walk close to the edges of the high bank looking down over the rocks and the debris which had washed ashore. Approaching Cleft Rock, she remembered how she had seen the gradual demise of that enormous rock on the very edge of the cliff. It had been several years ago when she had first noticed it. A small crack had appeared almost through the middle on its top edge and a small bed of moss had begun to grow in the crevice. Each year as the split widened the moss spread making a blanket of green in an apparent effort to conceal the crack itself. And then last year it was gone. The cliff underneath gradually washed away by the heavy tides had no longer been able to sustain the weight of the boulder and it had tumbled down to the shore below splitting in two. The dry moss lay burning in the sun alongside. She recalled the line of a poem that she had penned in her little scrapbook of memories, "even this shall pass away". Persons walking this same pathway would never know about the rock and the lesson she had taken from it.

This was the point of the Island that took the brunt of the storms from all directions and planks and lobster pots lay up against the trunks of several trees, some even hidden between the roots or caught up in the low branches. Some of the stunted fir, in an effort to keep alive, had continued to spread their branches. The strong winds had continually beat them down until they now spread horizontally like a huge mattress and one could stretch himself out and recline upon them easily without fear of falling through. Boys had used them as springboards jumping from them far out across the field.

It was to this poin. .nat she had come at the end of a day just to see the sunset on many occasions and then as the sun settled into the seas, raced for home so that she would be there when darkness had settled in. The three mile run was worth the satisfaction of drinking in the beauty of the glorious sunset.

PICTURE SECTION

B. K. Hichens

Wilson Trefry (cap on) and John Crowell

Hamilton cottage
(1981 photo)

Present Light keepers
quarters and generator bldg.
(1981)

Buildings and slip at east side
(1981)

Lobster pots west side

Church as it now stands

Inside of church (photo 1981)

Lindsay grave near church - replaced cross 1976

Graves of three women — unnamed

Original light (fixed)

Placing new top and light, 1902 (from glass plate)

Lighthouse with revolving light - 1902

Lifeboat, Howard Hitchens Captain

Wreck of Geo. M. Cook 1925 — Max Hamilton on prow

Cottages at west side (photo 1900)

Slip at west side

Brig rock —
balanced rock in center (1981)

Chapter 6

Finding a crate just near enough to the trees to keep her out of the sun now shining in its fulness in an almost cloudless sky, yet allowing her full view of the sea and Mud and Flat Islands and letting her feel the cool breeze from the water, she sat down and opened her lunch. As she looked out across the water to Mud Island, she remembered when the barquentine *Kingdom* had run shore there in 1910. The *Kingdom* was a missionary ship with men and women who called themselves "The Holy Ghost and Us Society" aboard. The ship was towed to Yarmouth and repaired. Later it sailed for the coast of Africa where the society members went ashore and formed a colony. She could well recall how excited she was when given the opportunity of going over to the small Island and seeing them.

She had taken a drink at the well between the houses at the West Side and that would suffice until she reached home. The dogs, all except Barney who was busily seeking squirrels in the thick growth of trees whose top branches nearly touched the ground where they had been bent by the vicious gales, settled near her feet. Donna with ears cocked and head erect waiting and listening for any uncommon noises, Buddy stretched out his full length his head resting on his front legs, and little Maggie, who in spite of her age ususally kept a few paces ahead of her, now peered up into her face with a look of satisfaction now that they had stopped for awhile.

Here in several areas were locations that had been named after incidents or wrecks. There was Little Beach where the *Vulcan*, a lumber laden brig, had been wrecked in 1830; the Mayflower, named after a brig bearing that name, met its demise here in 1873; and Valpey's Cove, named after Captain

John Valpey whose body along with his mate Ezra Churchill was washed ashore in 1806 after their brigantine the *Hibernia* was wrecked on Mud Island.

It was at Valpey's Cove that the *Bessie Wells*, Robert Porper, Master, and his cook named Cooms, struck in 1885. This wreck, for some reason or other, had prompted her to copy beneath its recording the verse from Kemp's Chanties:

"We brought his seas-chest aft with all it stored
(the custom when a man goes overboard).
It held the usual things that sailors own;
But at the bottom in a box alone,
We found a woman's picture — and we knew
Now why he'd been so offish with the crew.
He'd written it as plain as plain could be
She went and married him instead of me."

All the way from the West Side to this point, she had tried to bring to mind the many, many ships that had foundered and were wrecked on the shoals. One, the *Mary Alice*, a three masted ship, met disaster just north of the West Side with $5000 in gold sealed in kegs aboard. The Captain did not trust his crew so had planks laid over the kegs. Grandfather Crowell walked the planks all night with a loaded revolver.

In the years between this wreck and the demise of the rumrunner in 1924, many other vessels met their doom in this area, among them the *Willie* a brig loaded with lumber which was a total loss, and in 1900 the *Turbin* coal laden, which John Crowell, her father, was watching from the top of the lighthouse. He turned to light the lamp and when he looked again she was gone. All hands perished.

It was in this same area that, in 1870, the *Alexander William* a 166 ton brig built in 1866 bound from New York for Newfoundland with a cargo of flour, ran ashore in mid August. She was floated and taken to Yarmouth and became the first vessel to be taken on the Yarmouth Marine Railway.

She watched the gulls lazily flying just out over the sea, diving now and then when they spotted something in the water and lighting on a huge rock, majestically perched almost like statues, their gray and white feathers shining in the sun. Her
54

thoughts drifted to days long past when before and during her lifetime ship after ship had come too close to the point in the darkness or unable to cope with the violent winds had been swept into the rocks and battered to bits. It was at Race Point in 1924 that a rum runner the *George M. Cook*, Cook master, trying to escape the government ship had cleverly eluded its pursuer and then met its Waterloo as it attempted to round the point. Unlike their reaction to other shipwrecks when there was a great loss of cargo and sometimes crew, she had noted in her book of shipwrecks, that when learning of this wreck "everyone was happy". She treasured a snapshot of Max, her son, standing on the prow of the battered ship.

It was at North East point that tinkers and pieces of metal from various ships lay amongst the rocks or had been washed up over the high banks and blown into the woods.

Across the water she could see the sandy beaches and the rocks farther back on Mud Island and to the west of it the houses jutting up almost is if from the sea itself, Flat Island. It was between and adjacent to these islands that the lobster fishermen hauled most of their catch. During the winter and early spring, buoys of all colors bobbed merrily on the waves and thousands of traps, usually two on a trawl, lay on the ocean bottom waiting for the lobsters to crawl in after the bait and be entrapped. Hermit crabs in their conical shell homes often filled the traps along with their tasty friends. Now with the season over, the sea was clear and with the tide nearly at its low point, only an occasional white cap added contrast to the blue and green of the water. When younger, and her sight was better, she could see the mainland on clear days like this from the North Point all the way back to her home. This was one of the signs of her growing old, unable to see things which had once been so visible to her.

It was here one day that she had composed a verse, sort of an epitaph, even though she had never told anyone, but had copied it in her little book of memories and anecdotes:

> "When I quit this mortal shore
> And mosey round North End no more,
> Don't weep, don't sigh and don't you sob
> I may have struck a better job.

Don't go and buy a large bouquet
For which you'll find it hard to pay,
Don't tell the folk I was a saint,
Or any old thing that I ain't."

The breeze at the point was rather brisk but not chilling and she decided to let her jacket stay where it was around her waist as she placed the wrappers back into her bag and, folding it carefully, tucked it into her pants pocket leaving her pail empty. The most of the last sandwich had been doled out to the dogs and they stood there looking up into her face awaiting the next move. Barney, more impulsive than the others, rose suddenly and lapped her cheek in a token of love and companionship, and hardly had she reached to stroke his back, he was off into the wood in pursuit of another squirrel. His barking rent the still air as she rose to her feet, brushed off her clothes, and started along the path. Impulsively she scolded as he left her side but her voice was drowned out by his constant yapping.

Keeping back some distance from the edge of the cliff and the jagged edges where the tides had washed the soil from underneath the top sod, she tried to estimate in her mind just how far the shoreline had been pushed back since her first venture around the Island as a girl. Grave markers of those buried here after being washed ashore had long disappeared, and, not in a sense of humor but simply as a matter of fact, she had often referred to them as going back to sea once more. She had no idea, nor knew of no one that did, except God, as to how many bodies had been buried here down through the years nor how many unmarked graves still remained. In the records she had found, kept by Richard Hichens and others following him including those she kept herself, she had compiled a list of 187 ships that had gone aground or were wrecked on the shoals around the whole Island. The attic of her home near the Lighthouse, which she had been forced to evacuate when her husband died, had been full of relics from the scores of these vessels and had been left behind her when she moved to the smaller house in which she now lived. She still retained silverware, plates, odds and ends in the parlor cupboard to

56

show to interested visitors to her Island. The fishermen and lifeboat crews' families had also kept items that could not be used for food or clothing at the time collected.

Here at High Bank, so called, the schooner *Alice* was wrecked in 1894. She was only five years old at the time but she could well remember her mother taking care of the Captain who was sick with erysipelas in his face. She could not remember his name but in her mind's eye she could see her mother gently putting cranberry poultices on the affected area, as she stood back and watched intently. Somewhere among her possessions was a large picture salvaged from the schooner.

Even more vivid in her memory was the spring of 1921 when the *Mary P. Hardy,* a seventy-seven ton vessel, captained by a man named Tobin, was wrecked here and was a total loss even though the equipment on board was saved. The crew came to the cottage and stayed there until picked up by a boat from the mainland a few days later. Giving up her room to crew members, she had taken her infant son, John Maxwell, and made up her bed on the kitchen floor but the baby boy would have none of that. He screamed constantly. In order to keep him quiet and give the shipwrecked men their well deserved rest, she sat in a chair and held the child for three nights. Only God could have given her the strength to keep up with each day's activities in providing meals for the men after losing so much sleep. How little she realized at the time how precious those moments with her baby would be in her memory when she recalled years later the short time she had him before he died at twenty-one years of age. All the dreams of his carrying on the family tradition as lighthouse keeper, or whatever plans he had made for his own future, swept away and so soon after the death of his father. The nights that she had sat in the kitchen chair rocking to still his fears, the growing up years when she had watched him grow into manhood, and her husband's pride in his only son, were treasures buried deep in her heart to be remembered over and over again.

Before his departure, the Captain presented her husband with twenty new barrels to pay for his crew's board and room but somehow another man got the barrels. Written under account of the *Alice* in her book the shipwrecks, she had penned "All is fair in love and shipwrecks".

A dozen sheep, heavy with their winter's growth of wool, darted suddenly in front of her followed by Buddy, the larger of the dogs. With her sharp whistle followed by a cry of "Bud, leave them alone", the dog stopped and came to her. The sheep, momentarily pausing at her whistle, plunged into the thick growth of trees once more. Following them to the trees, she peered through the maze to see that none had been caught by the low branches. Satisfied that all had safely disappeared, she went back to the path and continued on. It wouldn't be long before the sheep shearer and his family would be coming over from Chebogue with their dogs to round up and shear the sheep. It was a task she used to look forward to herself but there were too many and she was getting too old to handle them alone.

It was just about here, she recalled, that she had come upon the big ram caught in a hole where the ground had been undermined by a spring that had since dried up. Even though it weighted considerably more than her 95 pounds, she, realizing that it might hurt itself, attempted to pull the struggling animal out of the hole. Though she pulled and tugged, she made no progress and the bleating of the ram added to her dilemma. Suddenly she felt herself slipping and down she went into the hole. Fortunately, the ram had turned and was struggling to get out on the far side as she slipped, and she did not go under his feet. Feeling the support behind him, the animal stopped his thrashing and in that moment of inactivity, she made her decision. Slowly she slid deeper into the hole under the animal's body and, as if sensing that he was being helped, the ram kept still. It was hard for her to get enough air to breathe under his thick coat of wool but deciding that she was under him enough for support she began to lift herself slowly, her head bent low and the broadness of her back lifting him slowly up from the depths of the hole. It seemed that her back was about to break but to give up now would only cause the ram to settle back on top of her and suffocate her. With a final thrust, she arched her back and with a spring that sent her flat against the bottom of the pit, the animal went out of the hole and with a bleat of thankfulness went off into the woods. Lying there exhausted, bruised, but not badly hurt to the best of her knowledge, she looked up into the bright blueness of the sky and softly whispered, "Thank you Lord."

The shearing pen was just ahead of her and she entered the small shack adjacent to the pen where bags and tools were kept. There were a couple of chairs and a small table inside and she settled contentedly into the larger chair. Little Maggie settled at her feet and Donna stationed herself at the door looking out toward the ocean where the gulls were flying and scrapping over tidbits uncovered by the receding tide. Buddy was off into the woods or perhaps had even gone on home after being rebuked for chasing the sheep, and Barney's barking echoed back and forth as he busily harrassed his twentieth or perhaps twenty-first squirrel of the day. Her legs were getting just the slightest bit tired but she knew that she had plenty of strength for the rest of the journey, about three quarters finished now. She had made good time and the sun's position told her that it was between one and two o'clock. The tide was low or just turning. She should be home in another hour and a half at least giving her plenty of time to weed the carrots before suppertime feeding of the dogs and sheep.

The air was cooler with the changing of the tide and the trees somewhat taller here on the higher level of the North East side gave more shade so she untied her jacket and slipped it on. The tools, medicine, and pail, that apparently she would not have any use for having found no straggling sheep nor berries, she retied around her waist, careful that as she walked they would not bounce against her hip. Carefully latching the door behind her, she started home.

Chapter 7

Rounding the bend she came upon the gull fields where hundreds of white and grey birds flew excitedly a few feet above her head lighting nervously on the rocks along the shore or on the tree tops, crying frantically and fighting amongst themselves for tid bits discovered here and there. Down on the shore, up beyond the average tide level against the cliff's edge amongst lobster traps, hunks of washed up tires and old crates, were straw bowl shaped nests, most of them now empty, which the young gulls had vacated within minutes after hatching. Occasionally one cradled three eggs still unhatched waiting for the heat of the day's sun and the high heat of the mother's body at night to produce the baby gulls. Once hatched, their little grey downy bodies, mottled with black spots, blended perfectly with the small rocks piled up around the shore, protected against larger birds or animals of which there were not too many on the Island. There were no animals except the sheep, rabbits, squirrels, the dogs and three cats, who never left the area around the houses by the Lighthouse and church. Occasionally an extremely high tide, evidenced by the borderline of driftwood and rocks, would lap at the base of the cliff washing the nests out to sea but at this time of year, and gull wisdom seemed to know it, the nests were usually safe from the tidewaters. On the rocks off shore, several seals sunned themselves, enjoying the warmth on their slick bodies, then slipping effortlessly into the water and soon crawling back for more sun basking.

Up on the grassy almost open field, surrounded by thick woods on one side and a border of trees on the other, hundreds of these cone shaped nests lay in the open sun unprotected against the elements, human or animal prey. The field was a beehive of activity on and above ground. Here young gulls huddled together giving the appearance of a mound of clay or a stone whenever danger presented itself, such as the dogs now running around, yet not bothering with them in any way. Barney would sometimes break an egg but several admonitions had discouraged his bothering the nests. With danger past, the mother would swoop down on her own brood with pieces of fish and with heads turned to her approach and mouths wide open they would await the morsel to be dropped down their throats. How each mother knew her own amongst the great population of baby gulls was a mystery of nature. This portion of the Island designated as a wildlife preserve by the government along with the Lighthouse area were the only sections of the Island that she could not claim as her own. Even this portion was probably hers by ownership and she could endorse the rights of protection for these beautiful birds. Why the fishermen and moss rakers found sport in shooting at them with their guns, she could never understand. They were not used for food and it was in fact unlawful to shoot them but here on the Island away from the authorities, laws made little difference.

Beyond the gull fields with the cottages between her home hidden among the trees and the shoreline now in plain sight; the church on the hill white against the blue sky; and the pier rising to its full height at low tide, now part of the scene beyond her, she started her gradual descent from the cliffs to sea level. This area was known as Head Yard for some reason never explained to her. Signs of any cultivation had long been covered by the growth of course grasses and flag lillies, but the story of Ben Hichens and the loss of his potato crop always went through her mind whenever she passed over this area.

It was in 1869, that Seal Island had been granted to Richard Hichens and Thorndike Crowell. It was also the year of the Saxby gale, a great storm that had been predicted two months before its occurrence by Lt. John Saxby of the British Navy. History has recorded that it left terrible destruction in its wake. Tides, world over, rose to unheard of heights. In the summer of that year, Ben Hichens had carefully tilled the ground here and planted a large plot of potatoes. It had been long tedious work preparing the ground but his rows of plants blossoming in the mid-summer sun had been his pride and joy. The words of admiration from his neighbors on the Island had repaid him for his efforts even if he might never get a crop.

The northeaster came up suddenly, almost out of clear skies. It had been unusually calm that morning, the fourth day of October, and the fishermen had gone out early for their catch. The wind catcher was almost motionless and the usual activities of the day were being carried on.

And then it started!!! The first signs of the approaching storm were the whitecaps suddenly appearing out across the sea. Then one by one the fishing boats began coming ashore, the fishermen telling of the sudden change and the difficulties of getting their gear in the boats. Some had left their nets behind to depart in safety, and the anxiety for the boats still out on the ocean grew. The lifeboat crews were put on alert and the women were getting their clothes off the lines. The Lighthouse hatches were secured and the storm hit. The hurricane gales swept across the Island and the waves on the high tides pounded far up on the shore.

"I've never seen it come just this way," John Crowell said to Ben as they stood on the Lighthouse steps looking out over the turbulent waters, "seems to be coming crosswise rather than in direct N.E. course. It's certain to lay some trees low and pound that point where your potatoes are planted."

"Good thing they are high or they'd be gone for sure," Ben replied, "the rain will do 'em good."

It was over almost as suddenly as it had came up. The skies cleared and the rivulets of water washed along the little gullies they had made in the ground. The doors of the cottages opened and families poured out to look things over.

"The boys all made it, thank God," young Wilse Trefry, captain of one of the lifeboats, exclaimed. "It's a miracle, just the plain grace of God."

The wind had apparently not caused as much damage as the high seas. Very few trees or shingles had been disturbed. A few shutters had been torn loose and lumber had been moved about but most of the lobster traps had not been moved to any extent. The shoreline was a mess. Rocks had been

62

washed up even against some of the cottages. Debris was piled high on the shore and seaweed clung to the sides of the trees and buildings. The path between the inland pond and the ocean was still covered and the pond itself seemed to be joined to the sea. Farther up along the cove, the low fields were still inundated and beyond that ?

In the late afternoon as the tides receded, Ben Hichens and his four year old son walked the path, mud up to their ankles, to his potato patch. He had seen from the slip near the church that the green and yellow of the dying potato vines weren't visible through his glasses and he had to have a closer look. The banks of the cliff hadn't washed away as far as he could determine but the land above looked desolate. As they neared the garden, they stopped and as one gasped in astonishment.

Where there had been a plot of dying potato vines yesterday afternoon when he had scooped up a hill with seven potatoes ranging in size from three inches across to the size of a plum, there was nothing but bare ground furrowed by little rivulets of water washing toward the edge of the cliff. Not even a trace of a vine or potato could be found. There was no sign that there had ever been a garden here at all, save that the ground was bare of sod such as surrounded it on the three sides.

"It's all gone, Daddy, all gone!" the boy looked into his father's eyes and he was almost in tears.

"The Lord works in mysterious ways His wonders to perform," his father answered more to himself than to the boy beside him. "Just see His power. All the work of my hands through the summer months gone in one sweep of His hand — what marvellous power — a marvellous God."

"But." The boy was silenced almost as the words of protest started from his lips.

"Ours not to question, boy, just trust, that's all, just trust."

All through his life, as she recalled, Ben Hichens' life had been one of trust. No questions asked.

The rest of the way along the shoreline where the water came a little higher up on the long expanse of sand drying in the sun before being washed away again by the tides was rich with history. History of shipwrecks, family and personal adventures. Each step seemed to revive a memory of the past.

Just at the dwindling line between the rocky coastline and the first of the sandy beaches on the East side, the incoming tide washed around the rusty engine of the 66 ton schooner *Elk*. Imbedded in the sands and securely fastened between two rocks it had withstood the tide and storms for thirty years since that September night in 1944 when fog had enveloped the Island laying an almost impenetrable blanket over the surrounding area.

She had remembered that day as one so different from those of the past when wrecks were reported. Communications had changed considerably in the past decade, 1934-1944, as had the means of rescue. Even though the light and whistle were still of great importance to the ships passing the Island and surrounding shoals, the radio was the big factor in warning ships and also receiving distress calls from them. And so it was on this night, that without advance warning the *Elk* neared the Island without any indication whatever that she was in the vicinity. Today the radar signals would have disclosed her presence in the area and with all these modern precautions and signals there hadn't been a disaster since 1955 when the *Jebedee M* foundered off Elbow Rock midway between the Island proper and Blonde Rock and the *Ayorlite* with a cargo of coal had struck at Green Head.

She had just begun to dress as dawn came, even though it was Sunday, and had noticed that the fog was lifting some when she heard pounding at the front door. The girls had gone to the mainland the previous Friday on one of the fishing boats and she was alone for the week. Hastening down the stairway, she unlocked the door and opened it to find Wesley Swim who lived in the cottage by the shore (now called the birdwatchers' home).

"There's a wreck up at the cliff," he excitedly shouted at her, "went outside to the spring and saw its outline in the fog, thought I'd tell you before I went up," and he turned and ran down the steps.

"Do they know at the light?" she called after him and wondered whether his raised arm meant yes or no, before he

64

disappeared amongst the trees. The dogs excitedly gathered around her as she led them into the kitchen. Brushing back loose strands of hair, she took her jacket from the hook, set her weathered hat on her head and latching the door behind her to keep the dogs in, followed after the departed fisherman.

Her question about whether the grounded vessel had been seen by others was answered as several men and women joined her as she hastened up the narrow roadway between the ocean and the fresh water pond, past the two sandy beaches to the fork where one path led to the West Side and the other to Race Point and to the base of the cliff rising some thirty to forty feet above sea level. Coming to a halt among earlier arrivals, she stood watching the bobbing lights as the power boats approached shore loaded with salvage from the ship. There was no sign of anyone whom she could identify as crew men on or around the vessel which was securely mired. Walking up to her close friend, Dewey Nickerson, she inquired as to the whereabouts of the crew. "Don't know," Dewey answered, "came up here 'bout couple of hours ago and there wasn't a soul aboard. Me and the rest of the boys figured we better get what we could off before the seas pound her apart." With these words he was gone.

There was all kinds of activity going on around her. Boats coming ashore with all kinds of merchandise: furniture, dry goods and so forth. No one had time to talk as they moved about in the heavy mist. The fog started to lift quickly and she could see the silhouette of the schooner imbedded in the sands. She wondered why there was such haste in removing the cargo. Couldn't it be floated again? Where was the crew? Almost as if hearing her unspoken question, loud voices came across the waters. She could see the small boats around the schooner and the raised voices of irate men. She pushed toward the waterline as a boat came to shore.

"Damn 'em! Why did they leave her anyway?" one of the Island men exclaimed as he waded ashore. "How did we know they'd left her and rowed up to the point? Blamed if they're getting the stuff back. It's our'n."

There was confusion everywhere as crew members and Islanders came ashore continuing their arguments over possession of cargo taken from the ship.

"Let her be until daylight and then we'll see," the Captain, a Mr. Barry, instructed his crew and those gathered around. "Everybody here?" he questioned and assuming that his men were safe, headed for the grassy bank above the shoreline. "Any food around here? Glad to pay for some vittles."

In response, several women came forward inviting the seamen to their cottages for breakfast. "Never saw such fog," one sailor exclaimed. "Been by here before but never nothing like this."

"Where are you from?" one of the women inquired. "From Gloucester, headed for Newfoundland. Thought we were on a ledge when we grounded. Took off in the dories and rowed up to the point for the night. Wasn't too bad after we built our fires and crawled under the overturned dories. Never expected to come back and find this." He looked at the piles of salvaged goods the Islanders had brought ashore. "Got to get this straightened out somehow."

All day long the removal of the ship's treasures continued with little or no protest from the Captain who apparently realized that his ship would never return to sea again. The impact as it hit the beach had loosened the timbers so badly that the attempt to pull it back into the water would just pull the whole ship apart.

The following morning, Lawrence Newell took the Captain and his crew members to Yarmouth along with her and her beautiful collie Jack.

As the fall and winter days passed, the ship gradually disintegrated into the sea. The relics; including the Captain's chair and an overhead lamp which graced the living room in her cottage (due to the generosity of an old friend), along with the engine now being washed by the incoming tide were the only tangible reminders of the wreck still existing. Even that was more than was left from most of the wrecks around the Island.

The short expanse of sand gave way to a smaller area of rocks as the shoreline curved east. Up on the grassline bordering the beach, she could look across the heath, the swampy area which had once been known as Cranberry Pond, to the rocky breakwater over which she had crossed some three of four hours earlier on her way to Race Point. She had picked bushels of bright red berries in past years by this pond but as the pond gradually dried up, the cranberries became extinct.

Here in 1921, she and Mrs. Clifford Nickerson, her old school teacher, had seen the small skiff which had landed on the beach during the night after leaving the 60 ton *Josephine DeCosta* which had struck Blonde Rock. Running to it, they had discovered the bodies of two members of the crew who had been drowned by the high waves sweeping over the boat as it had been swept to shore. They hauled the bodies the half mile or more to the church in hand barrows, washed the blood, sand and kelp from the seamen's faces and put pillows under their heads so that they would look better when the others came.

Several small flocks of sheep grazed contentedly on the marsh grass and it was difficult to distinguish them from the boulders scattered here and there on the moor. Gulls which had been circling overhead suddenly settled on the salt water pond and their companions seemed to be chiding them for taking a resting period. Up on the ridge of the rocks between the two sections of the Island, she could see what appeared to be a line of sheep crossing from one point of land to the other, In earlier years she could have distinguished them clearly, but at this ominous sign of old age, they seemed silhouetted against the sky line. It bothered her to realize that her sight was failing somewhat, but then, few people of her age didn't need glasses either to read or see long distances. Thus far in life she still had her own teeth and had never worn a pair of glasses. Occasionaly she did use her magnifying glass to read small print but never when anyone was present to see her. To the left of the ridge she could see part of the roof and side of the first of the fishermen's houses. The wooden shingled roof almost reaching to the ground and the unpainted shingles stood gray against the sky and she remembered how pleasant a sight it was to spot the house as she walked from one side of the Island to the other with an urgent message or on an emergency errand.

Chapter 8

Her path took her past the round of the shore where the largest expanse of sandy beach on the Island glistened in the sun. Many times she and the other children of the Island had picnicked on this beach and had waded into the waves ever mindful of the parental admonition not to wade too deep because of the undercurrent. To her way of thinking, the water was much too frigid to swim in or to remain wading in for a long period of time but braver souls had enjoyed the cold water and she could see their purple shivering bodies as they raced back up on the shore goose pimply and shivering with the cold. Although it had been years since she had even waded in the water, she could remember the odd and almost scary feeling of standing knee deep, taking a deep breath as the incoming wave went up around her thighs and then feeling the sand wash out from under her feet as the undercurrent sucked it back out to the sea. To her knowledge no one had ever been drawn into the sea by the swift receding tide but the warnings of her parents and chums seemed to ascertain that someone, sometime had been swept off their feet and drowned.

The waves lapped around the partly submerged spars of the *Louis Cottingham* which had laid here on the sands for over fifty years. She could plainly see in memory, her father rushing into the house on that winter's day, January 18, 1918, shouting that he had spotted a ship in a wrecked condition, from the top of the Lighthouse, after it had foundered southwest on the Island. Availing himself of the newly installed telephone cable between the Island and the mainland, he had called the station at Yarmouth. A tugboat arrived and towed the *Cottingham* to the East side where she was beached. She remembered standing right here on this shore as the battered hull was towed in. One mast and all of the sails had been carried away by the wind and raging seas and the lifeboats were gone. All hands had perished. The cargo of lumber had long since disappeared and there was nothing left but the hull. Beached here, the seas had gradually torn the hull apart and only the keel embedded in the sands, with its ribs jutting up toward the heavens, remained as mute evidence of the disaster. After huge northeast storms they would be entirely covered with sand and then gradually appear months later.

During the winter months, back when she was a child, the beach along with most of the entire shoreline of the Island was covered by an ice wall, at some points thirty feet high, when the spray from the waves would freeze. Covered by heavy seas breaking over the ever growing wall and freezing in turn, the barriers would rise higher and higher. From North Point house and Crowell's Point one couldn't get over the wall at all and the sounds of the waves breaking against it was the only evidence that the ocean lay beyond the barrier. She recalled with a smile, the time when she had found enough rough spots in the ice wall to climb to the flat top and lying on her stomach peer over at the sea beyond. If her mother or father had caught her there , she would have been punished severely, the danger of sliding over the slanted sides into the sea was so great. It had been many years since the ice walls had built up as they once did, attributed, she had heard, to the warm gulf winds moving northward as the years passed by.

Again the sands gave way to a greater expanse of rocks and this expanse bordered Brigrock, a huge ledge that stretched from where it was hidden under the ground out some one hundred yards into the cean. She picked her way over the rocks and little Maggie dogging her footsteps kept close behind. Buddy had long disappeared into the woods in search of rabbits and would probably not show up until meal time. Donna had gone on home, it being so close at hand, and Barney's shrill barking could be heard up toward West End as another harried squirrel perched high on a limb saucily taunting him with its nervous chatter.

About midway of the ledge, she came to the huge rock balanced on about three feet of its narrower edge, extending up into the air some eight or ten feet. It would take three men touching their finger tips together to reach around the middle of it and the upper edge was wider than the base. Here it had stood for the past ten years on the inland edge of a pool of water three or four feet deep and nearly four feet wide in the ledge, resisting the winds and the higher than average tides which sometimes swept over the recess leaving a new supply of water. But it had not always stood this way.

The hurricane had come north in that September of 1964 from the Florida Keys, slowly making its way up the Atlantic coastline causing severe damage in the Carolinas, New York state, Vermont and Maine and finally heading out to sea across the Bay of Fundy and the Nova Scotia coastline. It had struck the Island at almost dusk and she remembered having looked up across the ledge toward the North End where the roar of the waves could be heard even from the cottage nearest the shore where she had been fastening the windows and nailing the door tight against the coming winds. For some reason that she couldn't seem to explain to herself as she thought back on it, she seemed to especially note the huge boulder perched on its widest end on the edge of the recess nearest the sea and how it appeared as a staunch bulwark against the onslaughts of the gales and waves. She even remembered how, as she stood there with the salt mist against her cheek and the wind in her hair, the words of the old familiar hymn "Anchored to the Rock" had come into her mind.

She had gone back to her cottage noting the sheep huddled as one huge blanket of grey wool with the trunks of the trees standing up as bed posts between them. Surveying the area around here carefully to make sure that there was nothing loose to blow against the house and wondering how her little bed of miniature asters would survive, protected by the wire fence against the sheep, but helpless against the salt spray now blowing harder around the trees, she went up on the steps of her home, turned the brass ringed latch salvaged from the *Mary Bent* wrecked in 1888, and entered the house. Locking the door behind her she made a quick check of the windows by the staircase, spoke softly to the dogs all safely shut up in the kitchen, and entered the front room. The picture window just put in that summer by the man who had been working at the

Lighthouse, gave her an excellent view, narrowed as it was by the trees which even though hiding a broad view of the sea, provided excellent shelter from the N.E. storms. She lit the largest of the oil lamps, the one with the flowered base, and set it on the three legged stand by the side of the window. Settling into the swivel chair, a relic of the *Rob Roy* wrecked in 1918, made more comfortable by the patchwork cushion she had made during the long winter nights, she looked out over the ocean. Feeling thus secure in her little haven, she bowed her head and prayed for the safety of those still at sea, those standing by in case of emergency calls, and mother s-to-be who might have to travel in the storm to a hospital to give birth this night.

She didn't know what time she had mounted the stairs to her little bedroom on the South corner of the house. The wind was still howling and gusts rattled the windows and she occasionally heard a branch strike the side of the building but there was no fear in her heart. " Come what may, God was still in His Heaven." With that thought in mind she undressed, slipped into bed and drew the coverlet up around her. All was quiet inside the house in contrast to the fury of the storm outside and she drifted off into a peaceful sleep.

The quietness as the storm had passed by probably was what woke her. The red of the sky as the sun started to rise and the tranquility of the waters as she left her room and looked out of the hall window above the front door, was unbelievable. It seemed that she must pinch herself to realize how serene everything was after the fury of the hurricane as she had retired only a few hours earlier. As she descended the stairs, her heart again praised God for His watchfulness and care.

Chores completed, dishes washed and put away, following her toast and cambric tea breakfast, she donned her jacket, put on her weather worn hat and went out onto the front porch. The sheep were already scattered in small flocks around the field and the birds were chirping incessantly as they discovered new treasures blown in by the storm. Walking down the path from the house, contemplating the cement walk that she and Mary hoped to put in soon, she approached the shore. Driftwood, traps and debris of all description were washed or blown way up past the large cottage by the shore and she hastened to inspect the damage to the front of the house facing the ocean. To her amazement, there were no signs of damage on the house, the window was intact and not one shingle had been disturbed. It would take some time to clear away all the rubble piled up against it, but much of it would be used for firewood all delivered and ready to be cut up. Looking over toward the pier, she saw the fishermen already surveying the pier and slip, checking on their traps piled high beyond the tide waters and their boats pulled up in the lee of the wharf and fish house. Rather than get involved with discussion and sensing that nothing serious had gone wrong, she turned and looked up toward North Point. Starting at the farthest she could see, her eyes followed the cliffs down toward the cove and the path leading to the West side. Outside the traps and timbers etc. washed against the cliffs and some even blown up on the top edges everything seemed as she had seen it last night. She had recalled the story of Ben Hichens' potatoes but there was nothing planted up there now to be washed out to sea. Following the water line across the beach and then looking out over the heath everything seemed peaceful and at rest. It didn't seem possible that the turbulence could have abated so quickly but she had seen it happen time and time again and hours of labor had been required to clear up what a few hours of storm had washed up or destroyed.

And then suddenly she was aware of the great change that had taken place on the roadway itself. From the rounding of the shore at the long expanse of Hichens' beach, all the way down to the little cottage next to the one where she was standing, the sea had washed tons of rock up onto the shore and across the roadway. The East side was completely isolated from the rest of the Island as far as any vehicular traffic was concerned. Anyone walking would have to detour up over the hillside near the buildings on high ground to get from one side of the Island to the other. The sandy beach had disappeared and small rocks covered the area between the low water mark and the shoreline where it had been smooth sand. Unnoticed at first, she now realized that the beach area stretching to the

72

Burnt (or gull fields) had been stone covered all the way along. How they would ever get the roadway cleared again was almost beyond comprehension, but she knew that the men would figure out the easiest and quickest way after they had completed their duties around the pier.

At the sound of gulls circling nervously out toward the water, she turned her eyes away from the roadway and looked out over the ledge. She sucked in her breath in amazement. Almost as she noticed the change, she was running up over the hillside skirting the rock covered road. Heading down toward the rocks again, she saw the steam rising from the ledge in the bright sunshine. Recklessly she crossed over the rocks leading to the main ledge and came to the pool in the center. Hesitantly she reached out her hand and touched the huge boulder, which some had estimated weighed twenty tons, and stood speechless. For here it stood, up ended from the position in which it had been the previous night and now stood balanced on its smaller end on the opposite side of the recessed pool.

"By the hand of God," she reasoned, the mighty rock had been lifted by the waves, turned completely upside down and deposited some eight feet away on the other side of the pool.

Today as she stood beside it once more, she marvelled at the power manifested in its transfer from one position to another.

Chapter 9

Moving on down toward the water's edge where the breakers sent white spray into the air, she came to another deeper pool in the rock. Here as a girl she had sailed little homemade boats made by Ben Hichens' son and it had been told, although she had never seen them, that often at high tides the lobsters could be picked from the pool where they had been imprisoned. There were several levels some just like steps and wide enough to sit on facing the sea and hidden from view of those on land. When a girl, she had come here many times to sit in solitude ironing out her problems or just sitting looking out over the sea at low tide and musing over the future. And here on this aperture in the ledge, she had been given her first kiss.

She had met Ken when her father had taken her to the MacLeod's harness shop in Barrington. While the men had talked business, she had gone to the village store to pick up a few sundries and returning had stood just outside the shop awaiting her father and the ride to her uncle's house where they'd be staying the night. She had not noticed the boy until she had turned to see how the conversation was making out in the shop and looked almost full into his face. Embarrassed she stepped back to let him pass but he stood there grinning and slowly she forced a smile in courtesy.

"Sorry to scare you," he said, untruthfully she determined, for she was sure that he had intended to do so.

"I didn't know you were there, where did you come from anyway?"

"Oh, just out of thin air," he replied and his infectious grin seemed to wear her resistance down.

74

"You're Kenneth," she stammered striving valiantly to regain her composure. "You're his boy," looking in toward the man talking with her father.

"Yup, I'm Ken, sixteen, five foot eight, and one hundred and thirty pounds and you're sweet."

She turned as the color mounted into her cheeks. His frankness both irritated yet pleased her inwardly.

"Is my father through yet?" she asked quickly averting her eyes.

"Don't know, don't care. Let's go in for a cup of tea. Mother has it all ready. That's why I came out here, to get you and your father."

Mr. MacLeod, hearing his son's remarks, seconded the invitation and started toward the house.

It had been a nice day and as she returned to the Island the following morning, she lived it over again in her mind. The tea and pound cake had been tasty but the flavor had long gone, yet the taste of new love in her heart still lingered. They had hardly spoken to each other in the house and her father had rushed them out as soon as it was polite to do so. Standing by the wagon as the men said good-by, Ken had impulsively reached out and grabbed her fingers in his. With a gentle squeeze, he smiled and let her hand drop. So suddenly had it happened that she had little reaction but, on the way back on the boat, she could feel that squeeze, see the tender smile and feel again the instantaneous feeling that had swept over her body. The trip back to the Island seemed altogether too short and several times her father had to repeat his statements or questions before she answered.

"Are you deaf?" he queried and the blush that flooded her face and neck betrayed her thoughts.

Tom Crowell shook his head knowingly. His daughter was coming of age, attractive and alive. Even away on an island, one of these days some young lad would come after her from a fishing boat, government boat or maybe a harness shop. Ken MacLeod came of good stock. There was a possibility. Then with a shake of his head, he turned his attention to the course he was taking and grasped the wheel.

75

It had been a long winter and she had relived the experience of that meeting with Kenneth many times in her mind. She had come to this seat on the ledge often during the warmer days and looked out over the waters to the mainland. On clear days she could see the mainland shore and he seemed so close and yet so far away. Her thoughts drifted back tow'rd the occasion as she had lain in her bed 'neath the covering of the heavy blankets and listened to the sea pound up onto the shore underneath the clear moonlight skies on those bitter cold winter nights.

It was the following spring that she had seen the boat on the mid-morning horizon approaching from the direction of Shag Harbour, the nearest point on the mainland from the Island. Hanging the clothes in the fresh May breeze, she wondered who might be coming at this time of day, the fishermen already long out from the shore and no government boats expected until next week. Pressing the last clothespin over the corner of her father's shirt, she picked up the basket and headed for the house.

"Someone's coming," she explained to her mother, deftly knitting on another item for the fair scheduled in early June.

"Well, there's plenty to eat," her mother answered, as if that was the only problem concerned with new arrivals.

She was on the porch when the fishing boat anchored and a dory was lowered over the side to come ashore. There were five men aboard as far as she could determine but aside from the owner, Bert Shand, she could not determine those with him. Dressed in their oilskins to protect them against the spray from the choppy sea, they all looked alike, side and back to. And then, as one of them clambered over the side to jump into the small boat, she gasped in surprised delight. Ken had grown during the winter months and was as big as his father.

Their greeting was awkward but polite in the presence of the men when he bounced from the boat as it reached the shore but the look in his eyes reassured her that he too had thought of her many times during the winter months and his presence this morning was not one of duty. She did not offer to help with the few provisions they had brought along from the
76

boat, but stood back watching and wondering how long he would be on the Island and if there would be a chance that she and Ken might be alone for awhile.

Her questions were soon answered as Ken, leaving the group of men now increased by the arrival of Islanders, approached her.

"Come over with the Inspectors," he explained. "Heard that they were at the Harbour and Dad gave me permission to come with them. Will be here for about four hours or maybe longer, Inspector Hawkins said, and maybe if your mother's willing we'll stay for lunch."

"They always do," she quickly answered. "Do you have to be with them all the time, or?"

"Don't be funning," Ken interrupted, "my time's my own and I was hoping — "

"Just have to make my bed and tidy my room a bit and see what Mother wants me to do to help with dinner, but I think there'll be a couple of hours that we can — " Her cheeks reddened as a look of anticipation came into Ken's eyes and she quickly turned and headed for the Lighthouse path followed by the boy.

He was standing by the front of the Lighthouse when she returned to the yard sometime later. She had changed into a print dress, combed her hair and touched just a dab of her mother's perfume under each ear. Hearing her step on the porch, he turned and took her all in as she walked toward him.

"Gosh, you're pretty," he said quickly, and again the color rose up in her cheeks.

"Would you like to go up to the top?" she queried as he stood awkwardly striving to think of something else to say, and not waiting for an answer she mounted the outside steps of the Lighthouse and waited for him to follow. They were both puffing when they reached the top and stepped out onto the catwalk encircling the light, and for a few moments, just stood there taking in the panoramic view stretched out before them. To the south and west, the waters stretched out beyond the horizon and three or four small boats could be seen not far from shore. No freighters or cargo ships were moving this day as far as they could see and the waves were gentle as they rolled up on the shore.

"Its really a sight on a stormy day," she stated, "and scary when you see a ship away out there sometimes hidden by the billows."

To the north, the four mile length of the Island stretched before them. The hemlocks making a rough carpet over the rocky terrain as seen from this height. To the east, they could just see the upper part of the church steeple protruding above the trees and the path headed for the East side disappearing into the woods.

"Real pretty isn't it?" he said and started down the stairway again. "Isn't there somewhere we can go to be by ourselves and talk?"

"I know just the place," she replied, "where we can sit and watch the ocean and talk all we want."

Taking the short cut that led through the woods from the Lighthouse to the cottages on the East side, they walked the path, sometimes so narrow that their shoulders nearly rubbed the moss covered trees, and the mossy ground, sometimes bordered by large areas of bright red bunch berries, so wet that they had to jump from rock to rock to keep their feet dry.

It was along this pathway, since grown up, but kept passable by the few who knew of its existence and had reason to use it rather than the conventional roadway, that the lighthouse builder, Cameron, had hauled the massive timbers from the beach to the hill where the Lighthouse stood. With one horse, so the story had been passed down from one generation to another, he had managed to drag the materials through the dense growth, the shortest distance between the shore and the building site. How much help from others Cameron had received in hauling the timbers or getting them set in place, no one seemed to know. Yet everyone who had heard the story agreed that the Scotsman must have had extreme patience and a will to see the job done right to its final accomplishment.

The uneven terrain kept them so occupied that there was little conversation and it wasn't until they entered the clearing behind the Thomas house that they stopped for a few moments to rest. Ken reached for her hand as they started along once more but she quickly clasped her two hands behind

78

her back and moved ahead of him. Bryden Jones' wife had probably already seen them emerge from the woods land and would be conjecturing stories to tell at the next meeting of the women's circle, especially if Mrs. Crowell happened to be tied up with the lighthouse cottage duties and was not present. Daisy Jones didn't mean to be a tale bearer but the loneliness of the Island, away from a large family, sometimes could be alleviated by a little gossip and imaginative tales based on fact. Practically all the ladies of the Island took her talk lightly, but there was no need to give her too much to talk about, without asking for embarrassing moments at a future date.

Following the shore bordered by the rocks piled up by the storms, they soon reached the ledge and Ken deftly followed her past the balancing rock out to the water's edge. He soon realized what a perfect spot she had chosen for them to be alone together. A natural seating place over the waves breaking gently below them and well hidden from the houses. They could be seen by someone who might be looking out toward the end of the ledge, approaching from the West side but they would see the passerby long before they themselves would be noticed. She felt his hand on her shoulder as she slipped down onto the natural-fashioned seat but did not pull away as he eased himself down beside her.

"This is perfect," he exclaimed.

"Yes, it's a beautiful view. You can see so far out beyond the edge of the cliffs and I often spot seals and even an occasional whale while sitting here. I- - - "

"I wasn't thinking of the view especially," he interrupted, noting the color that rapidly rose into her face once more and felt himself flush somewhat as he realized the implication of his statement.

"You never told me just why you came," she answered regaining her composure. "Just accompanying the Inspector isn't exactly the best reason for coming way out here when there are so many things to do at home."

"If you want it plain, I came to see you," he declared and felt self assurance taking charge. "I have had you in my thoughts all winter and then when I learned that we were going to move to the States, I just had to see you."

79

"You're leaving Nova Scotia? You're moving away?" She gasped and couldn't repress the tears that welled up in her eyes.

"You actually do care for me, don't you?"

He put his arm around her waist and drew her close and she buried her face against his shoulder.

"I've thought of you so much and wondered if you thought of me," he continued. "It makes it so much harder to go away now that I know, but Dad has been given an opportunity to work near Boston and says he just can't pass it up. If I were only four years older I'd stay but he wouldn't listen to my staying behind now. Too many opportunities for a seventeen year old boy in Boston and none here, he says."

She didn't answer and he went on, almost as if talking could overcome the feeling that they both shared.

"But I'll be back, you can be sure. I'll be back and then!" He hesitated unsure of what to say and she raised her face and their eyes met. "I think I'm in love with you. Even though we've only seen each other once, it isn't as if we hadn't heard of each other and our families know each other so well, and - - - "

She put her hand up to his mouth and silenced him.

Quietly, they looked out over the ocean, watching the gulls gracefully flying around and then suddenly diving into the water after a floating morsel or a small fish; watching the white caps break out in the distance and then, forming one huge wave, pound in against the rocks beneath them. Suddenly a voice was heard above the noise of the sea and rising half way to his feet, Ken looked over to the settlement. One of the men from the boat was walking toward the ledge and calling his name.

"It can't be that soon," Ken exclaimed, "seems like we just got here. Or maybe it's just lunch time. Anyway we've got to go."

He reached down to help her to her feet and then as she rose to meet him, impulsively he drew her to him and kissed her hard on the mouth. It was so sudden that she didn't have time to resist him, but strangely she later thought to herself she hadn't wanted to resist him, not at all. Together they scrambled up over the rocks and made their way back to the shore.

Shortly after lunch, they made their way back to the boat with the others. Lagging behind, Ken squeezed her hand in his and quietly whispered that he would be back someday. He hoped she'd wait for him. He would write and hoped she'd write to him and he would miss her terribly. Within moments they reached the boat and he was gone out across the waters.

She had waited and they had written but gradually his responses grew longer apart and then after receiving a letter postmarked Cleveland, Ohio, in which he stated that he was going to college near Cleveland and would be too busy with classes to keep up correspondence, she received no more letters.

Two years later she heard from one of his cousins that he had married an Ohio girl, and five or six years ago she had learned of his death. But the memory of that short time together on the ledge, and his kiss, had remained throughout the years. Even though she had loved Ellsworth completely and gave her life to him, every time she passed the ledge or came out by it as she did today, the tender thoughts of Ken flashed through her mind.

Chapter 10

The roadway was mainly rocks washed up from the beach and she walked carefully along banging her stick ahead of her. To her right was the fresh water pond with scattered water lillies on its far edge. The decaying hull of a partially submerged dory and several battered lobster traps lay near the bank. Pieces of driftwood washed over from the extra high tide floated listlessly on the surface. This was one of the half dozen ponds scattered about the Island and perhaps the most popular skating pond of them all due to its proximity to the East side cottages. The largest pond was up on the West side along the breakwater but only the older children who didn't mind the mile walk, and wanted large surfaces on which to play their games, frequented that pond.

In the spring, heavy rains filled the roadway between the pond and the rocks separating it from the beach so that the water was sometimes a foot deep in the road and one had to walk on the rocks to pass by. Now in July, the water in the pond was down two feet or more from the sides of the road and only the small nettles and weeds grew up among the rocks on the roadway showing that there was moisture below them. She had spent many happy hours here after she had learned to skate well enough for her father to allow her to go that far away from the house by the light.

It was this pond that held the mystery of the surrendered guns of the crew of the British frigate *Blonde* beached on the rock named for it three and one half miles southeast from Seal Island. Some seventeen or more ships had met their doom on this ill-fated ledge hidden from sight in the middle of the seas, among them ships of war, schooners, cargo ships, Clipper ships and fishing vessels.

The story of the *Blonde* had been passed down from one generation to the other and authenticated in British and American history of the Revolutionary War. She remembered listening to Uncle Ben Hichens tell of the *Blonde* among the scores of tales he related about the wrecks around the Island and his many experiences, to the eager youngsters who crowded around his knee.

"It seems," said the old gentlemen with his graying whiskers accentuating the movement of his lips as he talked, "that the *Blonde* was one of the most active privateers along the Nova Scotia coast in the year following the Declaration of Independence. Her Captain, Thornborough, was ready to take his ship anywhere and attempt anything when he arrived. He was renowned for running down every ship and capturing men and ammunition. In May 1782, the *Blonde* captured the American ship *Lyon* captained by a Mr. Tuck bound from Massachusetts for Cadiz with a load of masts and spars, a very wonderful prize for the King's Navy. After sending the *Lyon* to Halifax under a British crew, Captain Thornborough, with Captain Tuck and his Yankee sailors as prisoners on his frigate, headed around the elbow of Fundy headed for more encounters.

"Of course, no one will ever know, but maybe the Captain was so proud of himself in taking such a rich prize that he forgot the dangerous shoals around these Islands between the bay and the open seas and wasn't on the alert. Or maybe the blame might lie on the ship's navigator, but none-the-less this frigate of the King's Navy struck and foundered on the uncharted reef and started to sink. That's why we call it Blonde Rock such as the other reefs and points around the Island are named for ships who met their disastrous end hereabouts.

"There are conflicting stories as to how the crew and prisoners reached this Island. Some say that they managed to reach this strip of rock and scrub forest, miles from the mainland, surrounded by the boisterous seas and engulfed in fog most of the time, by small boats or hastily built rafts. Others say they were picked up by enemy privateers and never landed here at all but from evidences of things found here, I am prompted to believe the first explanation and that they landed

83

here on the southwest side of the Island after braving the side rips and the pounding waves, with their small arms and a few provisions and camped in, contemplating rescue by another British vessel.

"But God works in mysterious ways.

"On the East side of the Island right here where we are, two of the very privateers that Captain Thornborough was pursuing appeared in the clearing fog and dropped anchor. Captains Daniel Adams of Salem and Noah Stoddard of Boston, masters of the Yankee privateers *Lively* and *Scammell* had discovered firewood and water on this ideal isolated spot on a hostile coast and had anchored here frequently. When the men came ashore, they discovered signs of life on the opposite side of the Island. At that moment a scouting crew of the *Blonde* investigating the Island area broke out of the woods and were immediately captured by the Yankee sailors. Just imagine how surprised Captain Thornborough must have been when instead of his scouts, Captain Adams and armed Americans appeared at his makeshift camp and demanded his surrender. After sharp bargaining, Captain Thornborough agreed to release Captain Tuck and the sixty American prisoners and give them a written safe conduct to Salem. Accordingly, Captain Adams overly gracious because of his easy acquisition of this great prize agreed to take off the British crew, leave them on the mainland near Yarmouth and furnish them safe conduct to Halifax. However, Captain Adams perhaps a little over zealous because of his accomplishment or maybe just not trusting his prisoners with any arms insisted that the *Blonde* crew must get rid of their weapons. Right here at Brig Pond, behind this stony beach, while Captain Adams and Captain Stoddard, their men and the liberated prisoners of the *Lyon* watched, the English sailors marched around the pond casting their muskets, pistols and cutlasses into the depth of the pond.

"But the capture of the *Blonde* didn't end there. The shipwrecked *Blonde* crew took passage to Halifax in a small Nova Scotia privateer, *Observer* and as they approached Halifax, she was overtaken by the Yankee privateer *Jack* of Salem, captured by Captain Ropes. Captain Ropes promptly attacked and got the surprise of his life. On the *Observer* were over 173 men all trained for the bitter warfare of their time and eager to engage in battle. Remember the *Blonde's* crew had been granted safe passage to Halifax, but all this was forgotten in the heat of the attack while Rope's shots whistled around them. After an afternoon's battle which was fairly evenly matched, the British sailors boarded the *Jack* and took her to Halifax. In an act of gratitude and thankfulness to God for safekeeping, Captain Thornborough released the Yankee crew of the *Jack* and they returned to Salem safely.

"Just think," and the old man hugged the two youngsters nearest him, "how God controls the affairs of men in such strange ways."

She reflected in her mind's eye how her father had told of the several attempts of Seal Island fishermen to find proof of the capture of the *Blonde's* crew on the East Side. Along with the muskets and other arms, stories of how the Captain's money chest and bottles of Jamaican rum had been buried in the slope around the pond sparked their interest and on several occasions they dug and dug and dug. They never found the chest but did discover several eighteenth century bottles. The corks had rotted and the rum was gone. Only recently, men from Yarmouth in diving suits and using metal detectors had gone into the pond searching for signs of the muskets, but nothing was found. Of course, the seas had pushed the rocks farther back onto the shore and the pond had been squeezed smaller as the years passed by. Maybe the very road on which she walked had been part of the original pond and she was walking over those discarded arms. Maybe someday the ocean itself would uncover them and the mystery would be solved.

Chapter 11

The walking was difficult on the rock packed road and the several loads of sand put in every year just washed down between the stones in the spring rains. In late spring, the roadway would often be under a foot of water for weeks at a time and machine travel would be impossible. One would have to walk on the rocks between the roadway and the shore for some two or three hundred yards or on the hillside where the two old houses stood gradually disintegrating with age and termites. The house on the crest of the hill was still sturdy enough to be occupied during the summer months but the wind howled around its corners in the winter sending cold drafts in around the windows and doors. The other house farther down the hill was well weather-beaten but with curtained windows to make it look presentable. It did add to the landscape as boats approached from the mainland. Mary and Jimmy had lived here for years after their marriage and Mary had high hopes of fixing it up to be lived in once more, but the foundation timbers were rotting away and there were so many chores that had to be done day after day that she doubted if the house could ever be used again. The old well with its weathered house covered by a broken board on strapped hinges still was the water supply for three houses in the immediate area. Its water was of red hue but still good for drinking, if one didn't mind the color.

She turned up from the roadway past the little cottage that stood almost on the road itself and on which they boarded up the windows facing the ocean every winter so that the rocks pounding against the building would not break the sash. As it was, one of the panes had a piece of shingle puttied across it to hold it together where it had been cracked across one side to the other. It was cheaper to patch it this way, even though it might not look as nice, than to buy a new pane of glass. She and Mary had promised themselves every year that they would paint the cottage and rent it to birdwatchers and vacationers to the Island and yet it stood unpainted and unliveable as each winter came upon them. Maybe some day soon it would be occupied again.

The dogs coming up to her soaking wet after cooling themselves in the Brig pond stopped momentarily while she pulled a nettle from the corner of the building, then bounded up the pathway to the house. A red squirrel having enjoyed their absence during the day scurried across the cement walk and reached the safety of the low branches as Barney raced after it and climbed six or more feet up the tree before dropping back to the ground barking feverishly at his prey.

Nettles were an obsession to her and more often than she wished to recall, she had vent her wrath and frustrations at the end of the day, or after a trying experience by pulling the nettles that had sprung up, it seemed almost overnight, everywhere. They protruded among the rocks along the roadway, surrounded the fishhouse, and old buildings and seemed almost to reach out and snag your pantleg or scratch bare legs as you walked by. She remembered how the whole yard in front of her house had been covered with the white and pink blossoms of the nettles and the deep purple of the thistles when she and Mary moved over from the Lighthouse cottage.

That was a day she didn't want to remember, the day that had ended the way of life that she had known from birth and seemed to hold only the promise of uselessness from that day forward, but she did remember. Many times in the darkness of the night, and in the mid-day sun as she watched men land and make their way over to the Light, the memory of that day kept coming back.

She had known this day was coming for a long time but never seemed to accept its actual reality until it arrived. She had known when her husband was taken from the Island and placed in a sanitarium, and an assistant Lighthouse keeper had taken charge, that someday in the near future she would have to relinquish her home next to the Light and move elsewhere to make room for the new keeper. But as the months passed by and things seemed to be working out satisfactorily, the evacuation seemed remote and secondary to the concern over her husband's health. And then a year later, when he died and she buried him in the little cemetery on the mainland, the reality came.

"I regret to inform you," the communication from the Engineer's office in St. Johns had read, "that due to the death of your husband, we must request that you find suitable living quarters elsewhere to provide living accommodations for Mr. Lewis Spinney who has been assigned by this office to serve as Keeper of the Light at Seal Island."

"I won't leave my Island," she had steadfastly protested to Mary and others who gently tried to persuade her to move to the mainland, "there's plenty of room around here. I was born here, I've lived here all my life and God willing I'll be buried here."

A month later she and Mary, their belongings transported in the old wagon that her father had built so long ago and pulled by the last remaining horse on the Island, moved over to the little cottage hidden amongst the trees on the East Side, vacated by the Thomases who had moved back to Clark's Harbour a few years back. She remembered how she had followed Mary and the men along the road from the Lighthouse to the East Side, along the slope where she had coasted as a child, past the schoolhouse that had closed its doors the previous June and past the church with its precious memories. No other day seemed as forlorn as that one had except for perhaps the day when the mail service to the Island had been discontinued back a year ago.

She remembered walking along the road recalling the many, many times she had run over this same pathway in anticipation of meeting loved ones, receiving supplies from the mainland, and the mail boat coming in . The sea seemed to be its greenest and darkest this day as if sharing her remorse and despair. On past the first of the houses beyond the old store and then turning up away from the shore to the cottage. The nettles were so thick that they stung her legs as she slowly trudged behind the rest and her frustration overwhelmed her and tears swelled into her eyes as a sudden hatred, an emotion almost unknown to her character, welled within her.

"I'll pull you all out, every last one of you," she declared vehemently and felt Mary's arm around her as she shook all over.

And the nettles had come out. Painstakingly with gloved hands or sometimes using an old bag wrapped around her hands and arms, she had pulled them out until the yard was cleared and the grass came out all sweet and green, kept like a carpet by the ever grazing sheep.

"Didn't you know that the thistle is the natural flower of Scotland?" someone had asked jokingly one day.

"And Scotland can have them all, and the nettles too," she had retorted, "every last one of them."

Gradually she had grown to love the little cottage as they painted it with a new coat of white and painted the wooden shutters a bright green that blended with the trees surrounding it. Gradually the hurt within had dissipated as she set up tubs on top of the old tree stumps and boulders and planted bright colored nasturtiums that blossomed all summer long. Gradually the activities around the Light became secondary as she worked in her little garden with her dozen or more hens and kept the woodbox supplied in the shed and behind the stove. Gradually this became home. A wooden slab, brightly varnished and with burnt-in lettering, "Century Farm" was fastened on the stump along side the cement walk. On the top of the six foot high stump set an old wooden tub overflowing with nasturtiums which she had planted this spring and in a few weeks would be brilliantly covered with yellow and red blossoms.

Chapter 12

She was surprised to note that it was only two-thirty when she stepped into the kitchen, the dogs almost knocking her down in anticipation of a snack. Barney was pushed aside and held down by Buddy who had never shown any inclination to be ugly with the smaller dog but just seemed to remind the younger animal that he was boss of the house. After holding him down a few moments, he jumped back and let him resume his antics. Donna jumped onto the couch, turned two or three times and settled down watching the others. Maggie, wagging her stub of a tail, shuffled under the couch and began to snore contentedly.

There was much to be done before evening!

First, she must call Mary and let her know that she was safely home, then build a fire and get the kettle boiling to make mush for the dogs and the crippled sheep and a cup of water to go with her toast. Mary had it so easy there at the Lighthouse with her electricity, just plug in her electric water kettle and in moments — boiling water.

Her dreams of electricity in her little cottage seemed to be in vain. So many times it looked as if she'd be able to push a button and have light, plug in a tea kettle and have boiling water, have a little hot plate to cook her food on, rather than build a fire everytime just for a snack, but her attempts to have wires strung from the power station at the Light ran into snags.

There had been the generator that the man from Halifax had arranged to have brought to the Island. Jimmy had set it up and they had wired the cottage for electricity. The dome light over her head and the switch by the door were reminders of their efforts. The hanging chandelier in the living room had been lighted once and now hung gathering dust. The television that she had bought had shown no picture for some time.

Oh, it had worked well.

But alone there in the cottage she had been apprehensive about starting it up each night and she couldn't afford to buy the fuel needed to keep it running continuously. So, there had been light and television on a few occasions and then she had told Jimmy to move it out.

The doctor who came with the birdwatchers had claimed that with his influence he could persuade the authorities in St. John to run the cable from the Light for her. "You deserve it after all the years you've lived and worked here," he had asserted, but she hadn't heard any more, even with all the praying she had done, faithfully trusting that one day she would have the wires strung and light would flood the little cottage in the darkest night. "Oh, that she might live that long to see this dream come true." *

Discarding her jacket, she took the bottles of medicine and shears and placed them back in their proper niche for future use. She hung the battered hat on the peg by the hallway door and proceeded to unwrap the cloths from around her ankles. She was relieved to feel the cool air around her legs which had sweat some, but it was worth the uncomfortableness of the sweating rather than experience the itch and possible poisoning from the nettles. Taking her "Daily Bread"

*In 1974, a Mr. Frank Campbell of Yarmouth, along with American friends rented the birdwatchers' cottage while they were engaged in diving operations off shore. Mrs. Hamilton did everything she could to make their stay a pleasant one, even baking several of her layer cakes to satisfy their sweet tooth. It was during one of their conversations with her that the men learned of her utmost desire for electricity and they decided to provide it for her. After Mr. Campbell had obtained permission from Captains Carnes and Shiels of the Department of Transport, St. John, New Brunswick, to place wires from the Lighthouse to the East Side cottage, the Americans came to the Island in 1975, cut a path between the buildings and laid the wires between the Light and the cottage. In further expressions of thanks for the hospitality proferred to them the previous year, they presented the gracious little lady with several electrical appliances to help make her life easier during her last years on earth.

devotional book, she opened it to July 2 and began to read the scripture preceding the short devotional message for the day: "This is the day that the Lord hath made, I will rejoice and be glad in it."

"How appropriate," she thought as she read the author's description of the many "taken for granted" opportunities one has each day, without realizing that it is all a gift of God's love. How related to her own every day existence, which she realized as she had taken her walk around the Island, was her gift from the Lord. How many people in crowded dirty cities, in the hot sultry climate of other lands or on lonely outposts throughout the world, would think that life on a small Island could be one's chosen life. But it was her life and she wouldn't exchange it for any of the other kinds of living she had read about or seen in books or on television at the Lightkeeper's home.

Audibly she read the thought for the day, "I will make of this day the best that I can and be thankful for it." What a wonderful day it had been! But the day wasn't ended. There were chores to be done, wood to cut, the garden to weed, maybe time to pull a few nettles and then a walk over to the Lighthouse and Mary's before dark.

After a brief prayer in thanksgiving to God, she rose, slid her feet into her better sneakers and headed for the garden. Untying the rope that kept the gate to her small backyard shut against the sheep, she walked toward the shed and barn where the old tractor, supplies, coal and grain were kept. The bins were almost empty now but the government supply boat would be coming in October or November with coal and grain for winter storage.

Past the buildings she came to the gate opening into her fenced-in garden, compeletely surrounded to keep the sheep and hens away from the plants. Undoing the length of bailing twine, she pushed back the gate and slid through into the garden. Rows of carrots, turnips, beets and lettuce planted in curving rows making almost a half circle rose from the rich black earth. Just recently thinned out, they looked vigorous and healthy. Between the vegetables and the fence were currant bushes which would provide several baskets of deep red fruit in mid-summer. Very few weeds grow amongst the rows and bushes, but down on her knees now, she searched for and pulled any sprouts that had dared push their way through the ground. This garden, close to the house, kept her and Mary supplied during the late summer and early fall, so that the crops from the larger garden could be saved for winter use.

After nearly an hour of weeding and thinning, she rose from her knees and after scrutinizing the currant bushes for signs of bugs, she made her way to the gate, carefully tied it securely and headed for the woodpile behind the henhouse along the pathway that Cameron had made to the Lighthouse.

The rows of carefully stacked wood, cut and split to stove length, had been leveled to just inches above the ground during the winter and now would once again be gradually built up to dry out for the next year's use. Several piles of driftwood and hemlock logs surrounded the area and Mary had a good stack of stove lengths sawed ready to be split. Taking the axe in hand she reached for the first stick.

"Nothing like splitting wood to relax after a long day," she had explained to some visitors to the Island who had returned with her after a walk around the entire shore one day and sank exhausted into some of the chairs by the back door of the birdwatchers' cottage.

"You can think that way, but it's not my idea of relaxation," was the reply one gave her as she settled comfortably into her seat.

Thoughts of the day's experiences flooded through her mind as she chopped stick after stick to proper size. How many times she had walked around her Island couldn't be counted. The special trips she had made looking for lost sheep, walking toward Race Point in the late summer evenings to watch the sun go down and her swift return over the paths along the cliffs' edge ere darkness had settled, came vividly to her thoughts.

With a good sized stack of wood split, she put the axe away and started down the Cameron path toward the Lighthouse. The walking was difficult at times as she had to pass through soggy spots and cross over real wet places on loose boards that Mary had put along the pathway. In a short time she came to the clearing, crawled between the bars of the fence and was soon in her daughter's kitchen. Drinking her cup of cambric tea and munching on the homemade cookies, she shared her walk with Mary and pointed out some of the things that needed to be done along the way. Refusing the invitation to stay for supper, she rose to her feet and headed for the door as the dogs crowded around her.

Chapter 13

She passed the garage and storage shed and approached the Assistant Lightkeeper's cottage which had once been home for the wireless operators. She remembered the summer of 1924, the year daughter Mary was born, when a marine radio beacon was established and George Robertson became the first radio operator stationed here. They had fixed a room for him in their own home which he slept in and operated his "gadgets" as she had called them. In the cottage down by the shore where the birdwatchers stayed was the little red swivel chair he brought with him to the Island and had given her when he left.

Following him were the Stidger brothers (first names she couldn't recall), M. Glouster, Raymond Butler who had brought his pet parrot with him, Leroy Dunbar, Arnold McLean, Herb Moore, George Owen, Arthur Young, Freeman Ogilive, Charlie Eyre, Earl McDonald, George Conrad, Murray Smith, Frank "Sparkie" Burns, Dan Waters, Art Stedman, Erin Brown, Harry Tomkins, Doug Jackson, Clarence Davis, Everett Monroe, Philip Dacey, Carl Polson, David Vail, and (as she had noted in her scrapbook) last but not least, Steve Ahern and his wife Ethel.

She couldn't fix a date in her mind when the little cottage had been built or how many of the radio operators had lived there but she remembered the many happy hours she had spent visiting with the Aherns in the little house, sharing with them the experiences she had known.

Just beyond the cottage was the gate separating the Lighthouse area from the road toward the East Side. The area had all been fenced in by the present keeper to keep the sheep from grazing around the Lighthouse and homes, necessitating the mowing of the grass around the buildings, which in her way of thinking was an added expense and a waste of time, but he was the king of his own domain, and she could not question his decisions.

Closing the gate behind her, after she had made sure all of the dogs were ahead of her, she walked slowly down the roadway toward home. The grassy center of the road was easier walking and she didn't have to be concerned with getting oil on her sneakers from the pipeline along the edge of the road through which the deisel oil for the generators was piped from the Government ship which came periodically. Along with the fuel, the ship was also loaded with supplies for the keeper and herself. As she walked along, memories of the many things that had taken place along this roadway, which had been "the store road" to her ever since childhood, flooded her mind. She presumed they had named it such due to the fact that most of her trips along this roadway as a youngster had been to Mr. Perry's store and that was the importance of the road to her.

It was midway on this lane that went downhill all of the way to the East Side shore that she had tried to avoid the men walking along the slippery path that cold winter's night as she, in her late teens, coasted with some of the younger children on their sleds. Swerving as best she could, she could not get completely around the younger of the trio and with a glancing blow knocked him off his feet and went sliding into one of the smaller trees. The concern for each other's safety overwhelmed them both as he scrambled to his feet and proceeded to help her up from the sled.

"Are you all right?" they both asked almost simultaneously, and she remembered almost too vividly the color coming up into her face as his friendly smile covered his. A strange feeling, not of pain, although her side did hurt a bit, swept over her, and blushingly she turned her head away.

"You're sure you're okay?" he queried once more, and she could do nothing but shake her head in the affirmative, lost for words.

Assured that she was all right, he turned toward his companions who had stood by watching the whole affair in an amused way, and with a laugh started to walk along the roadway. A few yards away, he turned.

96

"I'll be seeing you," he said, and the color which had been gradually subsiding rose in her face once more.

She did see him often as he returned time and time again on his fishing trips and then became assistant lighthouse keeper to her father and then, her husband.

It was adjacent to the lane that the first and only schoolhouse had been erected, and although the spot on which it stood had long since been overgrown with scrub trees, it was very clear in her memory. Captain Hichens had taught navigation to the young men who increased in numbers during the time the Lighthouse was being built. It had been recorded that he had twenty-two people living in his home at one time, including his family and students. Richard Thomas, her grandfather on her mother's side, a school teacher in England, was hired by her grandfather Corning Crowell, to teach his children in the big house at the Light, evenings. Following him, Annette Knowles taught the children of John and Corning Crowell.

In 1888, the little red schoolhouse was erected to meet the needs of the many families now living on the Island, and a succession of twenty-two teachers beginning with Miss Cora Nickerson, coming from Clark's Harbour and other points on the mainland, taught classes until the school closed for lack of pupils in the 1940's. Many of them were student teachers staying only a year, more or less, while others stayed for longer periods of time.

Her listing beginning with Miss Nickerson included Gertrude LeBlanc, Daisy Johnson who taught for many years beginning in 1895, Ethel Royce of Shelburne, Edna Sholds of Cape Negro, Matthew Devine, Pubnico; Burdett Crowell, Pauline Trefry, Barrington Passage; Edith McKay, Clyde River; Ina Knowles, Barrington Passage; Orpha Churchill, Elsie Aker, Hattie Spinney, Forman Nickerson, Joyce Flemming, Myrtle MacLean, Louise Barrows, Burgess Sabean, Rubie Savin, Thomas Carmichael, Truro, and Avita Burke, Sluice Point, who came in 1940 and was the last person to teach. She hadn't been sure in which order these teachers had served but had jotted down that Mr. Carmichael had forty-five students at one time. Both she and daughter Mary had been taught by Miss Daisy who retired when Mary was in the sixth grade.

97

She remembered her first day at school under the supervision of Miss Daisy who came from Plymouth, Yarmouth County, and the many years following during which she grew to love her teacher so much.

Among her prized papers were the letters from Miss Daisy to her father regarding the teaching position. Dated August 12, 1895, the first read:

Mr. Corning Crowell
Dear Sir:

Seeing your advertisement in the papers for a teacher, I hereby make application for the same.

I passed "D" examination last year and this summer have taken up all the "C" work. I have also taken a few quarters of music.

If you will please, and tell me immediately, whether you want me or not, you will oblige

Daisy M. Johnson
Plymouth
Yarmouth Co.
N.S.

The second letter dated August 22, 1895 read:

Mr. Crowell
Dear Sir -

I received your note last night. After consulting with a few of my friends, among them Mr. and Mrs. Freeman, I have decide to take the school for $85.00. I don't think I could really take it for less. It is a small school yet my same time is devoted to teaching, music and etc. If acceptable to you, will you please write immediately stating the way I am to come. I will be ready to go any week if you choose to engage me.

Most anxiously waiting for your reply, I remain

Yours truly,
Daisy Johnson
Plymouth
Yar. Co., N.S.

With her letters was her own little notation -

"Those who went to school to Miss Daisy, as everyone called her, always talk about it, seemed she influenced them for life. She was a teacher apart."

Just beyond the area where the schoolhouse and adjoining yard had been, was a large flat topped rock which had been named Lover's Rock down through the years ever since some of the youngsters had unexpectedly come upon Miss Daisy and her gentleman friend embracing in the late twilight hours of an early fall evening. She remembered joining in with the others in teasing the school teacher and enjoying the sight of the color rising to her cheeks whenever the incident was mentioned for sometime afterward.

She remembered the heartache when Miss Daisy, who was engaged to marry the young fisherman, watched him leave the slip one morning the following spring never to return. For the few days following his disappearance, the schoolroom, and indeed the whole Island, was a somber locality as eagerly awaited reports of the men's whereabouts were anticipated, but as time passed by the activities around the Island increased as summer approached and gradually life returned to normal.

Miss Daisy's fortitude, patience and trust in God through her great loss made a lasting impression on the pupils in her classroom as well as with her Island neighbors who stood by, helpless to do more than express their sympathy and supply her with baked goods as an expression of love. She later married Clifford Nickerson and taught at the school intermittenly until 1937. John Crowell built a house for them on the East Side, rent $30.00 per year. She died in 1951 after she had retired and left the Island to live at South Side, Cape Sable Island, in the house left to her husband by his father.

Almost directly across from the school yard area was a small water hole some ten feet square half hidden from the road by the scrub trees. She remembered walking down the pathway with her father and his dog Tat so many times. Almost everytime without fail, the dog would run ahead of them and swim across the pool, then wait, shaking the water from his body until they reached him. "We'll have to call this Tat's Pond," her father had stated on one occasion and Tat's Pond it had been ever since.

A rabbit that had been sitting in the middle of the roadway, darted into the bushes as she approached and Barney and Donna took off after it at high speed. There was a brief scuffle and then the two dogs barking in concert assured her that the animal had safely eluded its pursuers.

It was down this lane she and her mother had watched her only brother Leslie head for the slip to go lobstering with his companion George Smith of Wood's Harbour early that January morning in 1908. She had not often been up and around that early in the day when he took off in his boat, but this certain morning she had awakened and heard her mother around the stove, and had gone downstairs, to help with the early morning chores. With a fond kiss on his mother's cheek, the twenty year old lad left the house and turning as he approached the bend in the lane had waved to them as they stood in the doorway in the early morning light.

He and George never came back.

The men at the slip had assisted the young men in pushing the skiff into the water with its gear all loaded aboard, had watched it disappear in the fog and had gone about tending their own duties with their boats and traps. They were but little concerned when late in the day the lobstermen had not returned.

"Probably took their haul right over to Wood's Harbour," one commented and his companions agreed.

But the next day passed, and the next and the next, and then when men from Wood's Harbour and Clark's Harbour reported that the two had not landed at either pier, anxiety mounted. Fruitless searches were made for miles around the Island and the mainland coast. Patrol boats covered every harbour but no one had even remembered seeing them on the ocean that day they had left the slip or the days following. No sign of the boat, the men, or their gear was ever found.

Her mother just couldn't accept the loss of her only son. As time went on, she would pace the Island waiting for the boat to return, question every friend and stranger as to where her Leslie was' and even prepared special meals of his favorite foods in anticipation of his joining her at the table. Later after she had gone to his room to make and remake his bed,

100

someone would quietly put his place setting away. The sorrow of her brother's passing and her mother's mind going with him was a burden she bore for many years that followed.

The rays of the early evening sun sent streaks across the old boat house as she left the shadows of the wooded pathway, passed by the little telephone house and made her way toward the shore road and her cottage.

Chapter 14

Removing her jacket, she went to the back shed to get the dogs' food and mixing the canned meat with meal and water, she made a mush of the ingredients. Filling each of their dishes, she placed them in selected spots so that there would be no scrapping between them as they ate. She had learned from experience to keep Barney and Buddy well separated especially at meal time. Slowly and patiently she fed little Maggie, while keeping her eye on the others as they nosed around looking for any bits of food that had fallen around the dishes. Fully satisfied with the refreshments she had shared with Mary, she decided to pass up her usual bread and molasses supper meal. Possibly she would indulge in a cup of her tea and have a piece of toast before going to bed. She might be a bit hungrier at bedtime.

The dogs all satisfied and their dishes washed, she headed for the hallway and the front room. The shadows of twilight cast strange hues around the living room off the hallway as she, Buddy and Donna entered. Barney was still out worrying the squirrels who, as darkness fell, took courage to come down and forage for food. Maggie was content to curl up on her rug under the couch and dream contentedly of this day and other days when they had walked the Island.

The chill of the room, closed throughout the day, made her shiver momentarily and she drew her maroon cardigan sweater a little tighter about her. She would soon acclimate herself to the room temperature and be very comfortable. This was her room of memories. Her room to end each day, sitting in the rocker and thinking back on the day's activities and far back into the days gone by, or sitting at the table in front of the big window looking down the path and out over the pier and the ocean beyond.

She sat there at the large half-round mahogany table, laden with its books, old sea shells and sea urchins. Stones all polished and varnished, reflecting the light of the reddening sky, lined the windowsill in front of her and the leather bound binoculars that her father had used while at the top of the Lighthouse lay ready to be picked up and bring distant boats, gulls or the breaking waves to closer view.

Picking up her diary, scrapbook of momentoes, whatever one might call it, for it contained the clippings of papers and magazines, notations of certain events, poems she had copied and her own reflections of days gone by, she turned to the half written page, the next to the last in the book and wrote "walked my Island today, July 2, 1974 — Happy Birthday to me." Gently she turned back to the front and idly thumbed the pages.

"James Whitcomb Riley died today," we'll miss him. Underneath was a poem by Edgar Guest about Riley.

"Amelia Earhart passed over the Island on her trip around the world. I wonder where you are."

"Many people have visited the Island, some great, some famous, but all important."

"April 22, 1937 — The giant dirigible, *Hindenburg*, passed low over Seal Island as she had many times before. Exploded and burned as she reached her mooring mast at N.J. with great loss of life."

"I cannot respect a man who purposely steps on a bug on the path." Thoreau — "I agree!"

"Hydrographic service 2873 came and built nine towers (called stations) in 1960, were here two of three summers, then abandoned the stations to the gulls, the sea, and me."

Firsts on the Island

First horse owned by Cameron, Lighthouse builder
First bathtub installed by Mrs. A. Farnsworth Drew
First motor boat owned by brother Leslie Crowell
John Crowell owned the first radio
Herb Moore brought over the first car
Mr. and Mrs. Steve Ahern brought first T.V.
I had the first lawnmower.

So many times she had read these notations along with the many others and wished that she had written many more accounts and had saved many more clippings such as the one of the Coast Guard boat 101 and the rescue of the overturned fisherman in the stormy sea. All she had was the picture of the boat and its crew. Underneath she had written "Hurrah for the 101".

Laying the book down, she rose to her feet and reached for the lamp on the shelf along the window frame. Its silver base was somewhat tarnished with age and wear, but its light shone as bright as ever both illuminating the room and sending its rays out into the night as a beacon for those approaching the shore.

The glow from the lamp reflected on the cabinets diagonally across from each other in the inside and outsie corners of the room. One contained her books, some gifts, some borrowed, and others purchased on one of her few trips to the mainland. It was plain to see that her interests lay with the sea as the titles of the books, some novels, some fact, some historical, indicated. Books by Randall, the Canadian author of fact and fiction, Edward Rowe Snow, the Maine author, and poems of John Marshall, the English poet laureate, along with other well known writers of sea stories, stood together in the three shelves surrounded by photos and paintings of the sea and the Island.

The marble topped table with its many photos taken through the years sat in front of the side window next to the larger table crowded between it and the couch which lined the inside wall next to the storage shed. The larger table was piled with odds and ends, mostly pictures that people had sent her of Island scenes, magazines that she had read but felt worth saving for further reference, and sewing materials. As a catchall it was a last source of inventory when something she wanted couldn't be found elsewhere.

The couch, well worn, but covered with a dark green spread, was her resting place during the brief rest periods throughout the day which she realized were becoming more frequent as the years passed by. Here she could lie down and catch a few winks or just lie with her eyes wide open gazing at

104

the furnishings of the room, the treasures in the closet at its foot and reflect on the past; the Lighthouse days, the wrecks, the tragedies, and the many friends who had lived and died or left for the mainland in years past. Here, she could rise quickly at the first barking of the dogs should anyone approach the house or anything happen along the shore and pier that aroused their attention. Here was her haven of rest during a busy day.

At the foot of the couch sat the old Captain's chair rescued from one of the many wrecks and which had not been directly identified with any one. Alongside sat the old water bucket with its rope handles, garnered with other treasures from the *Ottawa*. She had varnished the sides in and out and had painted in white letters S.S. OTTAWA 1891.

A well aged sword from a large sword fish shared the corner with a sheathed sword given to her father by an old sea captain when he was a boy. The maple cabinet stood between the corner of the room and the door to the hall, with only room for the clock taken from the *William Abrams* between it and the door casing. The clock with its twelve inch face had long since ceased running, but she had understood that two other clocks taken from the wreck and purchased by the Baptist Meeting House and the Methodist Chapel in Yarmouth were still in good running condition.

The cabinet was filled. There were shells of all shapes and sizes, cleaned and carefully shellacked. Some she had gathered around the shore and others had been sent her by friends who had picked them up or purchased them in far off places. They had been carefully placed between souvenirs given her, or saved from the many wrecks. Dishes of all kinds, heavy plates, dainty English china, silverware, and even an ivory knife, salvaged from the many ships, lined the back of the cabinet, surrounded by several stuffed birds, their feathers still carrying a bright sheen, that her father had processed in his late years of life. In one corner was propped the thigh bone of a medium sized man, yellowed and smoothed by time, which she had picked up on one of her many jaunts around the shore.

She enjoyed watching visitors as they "Oh'd and Ah'd", looking at her prized possessions through the glass doors, securely locked to discourage anyone who might be tempted to handle them and possibly damage them in some way.

Returning to the chair by the window, she once more looked out over the sea, memories of the past, now more vivid to her mind since looking over the closeted possessions. Absently her fingers caressed the small leather bound book, her childhood diary. She had written on only a few of its pages, the greater portion of it still waiting for her handwriting, but probably in vain.

Her first notation December 30th, 1901 was written in fine penmanship for a twelve year old.

"It is thick fog today. There's a vessel ashore on the North end. Her name is *Oliver Wendell Holmes*. She had eight men on board."

December 31, 1901 -

"The steamer is here today. We are going up to the 'reck' tomorrow. It is the last day of the old year. We didn't get anything out of her at all."

January 1, 1902

"We did not go up to the 'reck' today. It is blowing too hard."

January 2, 1902

"I went up to the 'reck' today. One of the men gave me a plate."

January 5, 1902

"It is Sunday today. Ship Pond will be bare. I am going for a skate."

The opposite page was blank but on the following page her next entry was made on June 9, 1905.

"Henry Crowell came home today for a few hours and we were pleased to see him. He came in a gasoline boat.

Doctor Hichens is on putting a wire fence around a cranberry patch."

June 13

"I got a piece of wood that came out of the *Energy* forty years ago.
Dr. Hichens told me about it".

June 27, 1905.

"Only two more days for me in the little red schoolhouse where I have spent so many hours. I will be sixteen Sunday, sweet 16."

July 2, 1905

"In Barrington today sweet 16 one present."

July 4

"Went on spree up Barrington river today. Had the best time I ever had in my life."

Again an empty page and then on the following page, this entry almost a year later.

June 18, 1906

"Went for my first gasoline sail tonight in Leslie's boat and Chesley's engine. It was the first time I was ever in a motor boat."

And directly underneath, the final notation a year and a half later.

Jan 29, 1908

"Copied from paper. Leslie Crowell and George Smith disappeared while lobstering. Leslie only son of John Crowell 20 years old.
Ferry between Seal Island and Clark's Harbour in connection with mail service."

The remaining pages of the little book were blank, weathered and yellowed by time.
It was getting really dark outside and she was beginning to feel the weariness from the excitement of the day and her

vigorous activities. Reluctant to leave the day behind and go up the stairs to bed, she reached across the table for her Shipwreck book. On its title page, preceding the explanation of what the book contained and the date of its compilation, was perhaps her favorite verse written for her by a friend whose name she had forgotten:

Here on a lonely Island
Washed round by lonely seas;
Far out from sight of headland,
Soothed by the salt sea breeze—
Just why I'm here or where I go,
My heart requests but may not know.

I've walked around my Island
And found a place called home;
But often watched the skyline
With longing there to roam—
Yet still I ponder day by day;
Why am I here? How long I stay?

Upon a lonely Island!
Oh, 'tis not lonely here:
For now from out the skyspace
A presence seemeth near:
The clouds bend low and whisper
sweet:
"You're living at your Savior's feet."

Looking up from the book she suddenly noticed the beam from the Lighthouse as it swept across the steeple of the church on the hill. Reflected by the light the pointed steeple seemed like a scepter pointing up into the skies. A sense of a real closeness to Heaven swept over her and she bowed her head and offered a prayer of thanksgiving for the day she had experienced.

Rising slowly to her feet, she blew out the lamp and calling the dogs headed back to the kitchen to take care of the last minute duties before going up the stairs to bed.